The Law and Practice of Risk Assessment

The Law and Practice of Risk Assessment

A Practical Programme

Jeremy Stranks

MSc, FCIEH, FIOSH, RSP

London · Hong Kong · Johannesburg · Melbourne · Singapore · Washington DC

PITMAN PUBLISHING
128 Long Acre, London WC2E 9AN
Tel: +44 (0)171 447 2000
Fax: +44 (0)171 240 5771

A Division of Pearson Professional Limited

First published in Great Britain 1996

British Library Cataloguing in Publication Data
A CIP catalogue record for this book can be obtained from the British Library.

ISBN 0 273 62352 4

10 9 8 7 6 5 4 3 2 1

Typeset by Northern Phototypesetting Co Ltd, Bolton
Printed and bound in Great Britain by Bell & Bain Ltd, Glasgow

The Publishers' policy is to use paper manufactured from sustainable forests.

Contents

Preface

The last decade has seen increasing emphasis placed on the subject of risk assessment. Employers in particular have a legal duty to undertake a suitable and sufficient assessment of risk to their employees and other people under regulations such as the Management of Health and Safety at Work Regulations 1992, the Manual Handling Operations Regulations 1992 and the Control of Substances Hazardous to Health Regulations 1994.

Risk assessment, however, could hardly be described as a precise science. 'Risk' includes elements of chance and uncertainty, but is not defined in current legislation. The language of risk assessment is riddled with vague terms, such as 'probability', 'likelihood' and 'maximum possible loss' – all of which are subject to individual interpretation. Moreover, the guidance on risk assessment provided by the statutory authorities can only be described as limited. This means that employers have got to decide on a system of risk assessment which is appropriate to the hazards of the business and, at the same time, meets the requirements of current legislation.

What should be appreciated is that risk assessment is only part of the health and safety management process and, as such, does not stand on its own. It must be seen as an integral feature of management systems for health and safety and related to various forms of performance monitoring.

This book summarises the current legal requirements and guidance on risk assessment and puts forward a number of models for different types of risk assessment. I hope all those who use these models will find them helpful in terms of meeting their responsibilities with regard to risk assessment under the legislation.

Jeremy Stranks
1996

List of abbreviations

ACGIH	American Conference of Government Industrial Hygienists
ACOP	Approved Code of Practice
AER	All England Reports
CHIP	Chemicals (Hazard Information and Packaging for Supply) Regulations 1994
COSHH	Control of Substances Hazardous to Health Regulations 1994
ETA	Event tree analysis
FMEA	Failure mode and effect analysis
FTA	Fault tree analysis
HAZOPS	Hazard and operability studies
HSC	Health and Safety Commission
HSE	Health and Safety Executive
HSDSER	Health and Safety (Display Screen Equipment) Regulations 1992
HSWA	Health and Safety at Work, etc. Act 1974
ILO	International Labour Organisation
JSA	Job safety analysis
LEV	Local exhaust ventilation
MEL	Maximum exposure limit
MHOR	Manual Handling Operations Regulations 1992
MHSWR	Management of Health and Safety at Work Regulations 1992
OES	Occupational exposure standard
PPE	Personal protective equipment
PPEWR	Personal Protective Equipment at Work Regulations 1992
PSA	Project safety analysis
PUWER	Provision and Use of Work Equipment Regulations 1992
WHSWR	Workplace (Health, Safety and Welfare) Regulations 1992

1

The general and specific duties to assess risks

Risk assessment is the key requirement of the regulations that came into operation on 1 January 1993. However, this duty is not new. The duty to assess risks is implied under the Health and Safety at Work, etc. Act 1974 (HSWA) in terms of the general and more specific duties of employers under section 2.

Section 2(1) states:

> It shall be the duty of every employer to ensure, so far as is reasonably practicable, the health, safety and welfare at work of all his employees.

In order to decide what is reasonably practicable, he must, first, identify the hazards and, second, evaluate the risks arising from those hazards.

A similar conclusion could be drawn in respect of the employer's extended duties under section 2(2), in terms of plant and systems of work (section 2(2)(a)), the use, handling, storage and transport of articles and substances (section 2(2)(b)), the provision of such information, instruction, training and supervision (section 2(2)(c)), the provision of a place of work, including means of access to and egress from same (section 2(2)(d)), and the provision and maintenance of a working environment and adequate welfare facilities and arrangements (section 2(2)(e)).

Similar provisions apply in the case of the general duties of employers and self-employed people to those other than their employees (section 3), the general duties of people concerned with premises to those other than their employees (section 4), and the general duties of manufacturers, etc. as regards articles and substances used for work (section 6).

RISK ASSESSMENT AND THE REGULATIONS

A number of regulations made under the HSWA require the employer to undertake some form of risk assessment. For instance, under the Control of Substances Hazardous to Health Regulations 1988 (COSHH), as amended in 1994, employers are required to undertake health risk assessments. More recently, the Management of Health and Safety at Work Regulations 1992 (MHSWR) require an employer to make a suitable and sufficient assessment of the risks to the health and safety to which not only his own employees are exposed to while at work, but also non-employees 'arising out of or in connection with the conduct by him of his undertaking'.

Further information on the risk assessment process is provided in Approved Codes of Practice (ACOPs) and HSE Guidance Notes issued with regulations. The relative legal significance of ACOPs and Guidance Notes must be recognised, not only when dealing with risk assessments, but in the general interpretation of duties under regulations.

Approved Codes of Practice (ACOPs)

An ACOP is a quasi-legal document and, although non-compliance does not constitute a breach, if a contravention of regulations is alleged, the fact that the ACOP was not followed would probably be accepted in court as evidence of failure to do all that was reasonably practicable. A defence would be to prove that *works of equivalent nature* had been carried out or something equally good or better had been done.

HSE Guidance Notes

The Health and Safety Executive (HSE) issues Guidance Notes in some cases to supplement the information in regulations and ACOPs. Guidance Notes have no legal status and are purely of an advisory nature.

The various duties to undertake risk assessments are outlined below.

Management of Health and Safety at Work Regulations 1992

Regulation 3

Every employer shall make a suitable and sufficient assessment of:

- the risks to the health and safety of his *employees* to which they are exposed while at work
- the risks to the health and safety of *persons not in his employment* arising out of or in connection with the conduct by him of his undertaking

for the purpose of identifying the measures he needs to take to comply with his duties under the relevant statutory provisions.

Similar provisions apply in the case of self-employed people (regulation 3(2)).

He must also revise this assessment when it is no longer valid because of new or changed risks (regulation 3(3)).

1

Considerable guidance on the principles of risk assessment, the purpose of risk assessment, what is a suitable and sufficient risk assessment, the need for review and revision, risk assessment in practice, assessment under other regulations, recording, and the preventive and protective measures is provided in the ACOP accompanying the regulations. These aspects of the ACOP are covered below.

ACOP

General principles of risk assessment

3 This regulation requires all employers and self-employed people to assess the risks to workers and any others who may be affected by their undertaking. Employers with five or more employees must also record the significant findings of that assessment.

4 Many employers already carry out *de facto* risk assessments on a day-to-day basis during the course of their work; they will note changes in working practice, they will recognise faults as they develop and they will take the necessary corrective actions. This regulation, however, requires that employers should undertake a systematic general examination of their work activity and that they should record the significant findings of that risk assessment.

5 A risk assessment should usually involve identifying the hazards present in any undertaking (whether arising from work activities or from other factors, for example, the layout of the premises) and then evaluating the extent of the risks involved, taking into account whatever precautions are already being taken. In this code:

- a *hazard* is something with the potential to cause harm (this can include substances or machines, methods of work and other aspects of work organisation)
- *risk* expresses the likelihood that the harm from a particular hazard will be realised
- the *extent* of the risk covers the population that might be affected by a risk, i.e. the number of people who might be exposed and the consequences for them.

Risk, therefore, reflects both the likelihood that harm will occur and its severity.

6 In some cases, this detailed approach may not be necessary as all the hazards are known and the risks are readily apparent so they can be addressed directly.

The purpose of risk assessment in this regulation

7 The purpose of the risk assessment is to help the employer or self-employed person to determine what measures should be taken to comply with the employer's or self-employed person's duties under the 'relevant statutory provisions'. This phrase covers the general duties in the Health and Safety at Work, etc. Act 1974 and the more specific duties in the various acts and regulations (including these regulations) associated with the HSWA.

8 Regulation 3 does not itself stipulate the measures to be taken as a result of the risk assessment. The measures in each workplace will derive from compliance with other health and safety duties as described above, taking carefully into account the risk assessment. In essence, the risk assessment guides the judgement of the

employer or the self-employed person as to the measures they ought to take to fulfil their statutory obligations.

Suitable and sufficient

9 A suitable and sufficient risk assessment:

- should identify the significant risks arising out of work.

This means focusing on those risks that are liable to arise because of work activity.

Trivial risks can usually be ignored, unless the work activity compounds those risks or there is evidence of significant relevance to the particular work activity.

Employers and the self-employed are expected to take reasonable steps, such as reading HSE guidance, the trade press, company or supplier manuals, etc., to familiarise themselves with the hazards and risks in their work.

- should enable the employer or the self-employed person to identify and prioritise the measures that need to be taken to comply with the relevant statutory provisions
- should be appropriate to the nature of the work and such that it remains valid for a reasonable period of time.

This will enable the risk assessment and the significant findings to be used positively by management, say to change working procedures or to introduce medium- to long-term controls.

For relatively static operations, the risk assessment should be such that it is not necessary to repeat it every time someone is exposed to a hazard in comparable circumstances.

For more dynamic activities, such as where the detailed work activity may change fairly frequently or the workplace itself changes and develops (for example, on a temporary work site or where the work involves peripatetic workers moving from site to site) the risk assessment might have to concentrate more on the broad range of risks that might arise so that detailed planning and employee training can take account of those risks and enable them to be controlled as and when they arise.

Review and revision

10 The regulation requires employers and the self-employed to review and, if necessary, modify their risk assessments, as assessment should not be a once-and-for-all activity. The nature of work changes; the appreciation of hazards and risks may develop. Monitoring under the arrangements required by regulation 4 may reveal near misses or defects in plant. Adverse events may take place even if a suitable risk assessment has been made and appropriate preventative and protective measures taken.

11 The employer or self-employed person needs to review the risk assessment if there are developments that suggest that it might no longer be valid (or that it can be improved). In most cases, it is prudent to plan to review risk assessments at regular intervals – the time between reviews being dependent on the nature of the risks and the degree of change likely in the work activity. Such reviews should form part of standard management practice.

Risk assessment in practice

12 There are no fixed rules about how a risk assessment should be undertaken, although paragraph 16 sets out the general principles that should be followed. The assessment will depend on the nature of the undertaking and the type and extent of the hazards and risks. Above all, the process needs to be practical and it should involve management, whether or not advisers or consultants assist with the detail. Employers should ensure that those involved take reasonable care in carrying out the risk assessment, although the assessment would not be expected to cover risks that were not reasonably foreseeable.

13 For small undertakings presenting few or simple hazards, a suitable and sufficient risk assessment can be a very straightforward process, based on judgement and requiring no specialist skills or complicated techniques. At the other extreme, in the case of, for example, complicated chemical, large-scale mineral extraction or nuclear plant, it may need to be developed so far as to produce the basis for a complete safety case or report for the plant incorporating such techniques as quantified risk assessment.

14 In many intermediate cases, it will not be possible to make a suitable and sufficient risk assessment without specialist advice in respect of unfamiliar risks, such as those requiring some knowledge of ergonomics or the more complicated processes or techniques in the enterprise. And some risks cannot be properly evaluated without the application of modern techniques of measurement.

15 In some cases, a single exercise covering all risks in a workplace or activity may be appropriate. In other cases, separate assessment exercises for the risks arising from particular operations or groups of hazards may be more effective. In all cases, however, it is important that the employer or self-employed person adopts a structured approach to risk assessment.

16 In particular, a risk assessment should:

- ensure that all *relevant* risks or hazards are addressed
  - the aim is to identify the significant risks in the workplace, so do not obscure those risks with an excess of information or by concentrating on trivial risks
  - in most cases, first identify the hazards, that is, those aspects of work (such as substances or equipment used, the work processes or work organisation) that have the potential to cause harm
  - if there are specific acts or regulations to be complied with, these may help to identify the hazards
  - assess the risks from the individual hazards; if there are no hazards, there are no risks (some risks may already be controlled in some way, whether by deliberate measures or by the circumstances in which they are found) – the effectiveness of those controls needs to be taken into account in assessing the residual risk
  - be systematic in looking at hazards and risks – for example, it may be necessary to look at hazards and risks in groups such as machinery, transport, substances, electrical, etc., while in other cases, an operation by operation approach may be

needed, say materials in production, dispatch, offices, etc.
- ensure that all aspects of the work activity are reviewed.

- address *what actually happens* in the workplace or during the work activity:
  - actual practice may differ from the works manual; indeed, this is frequently how risks creep in unnoticed
  - think about the non-routine operations, such as maintenance operations, loading and unloading, changes in production cycles, etc.
  - interruptions to the work activity are a frequent cause of accidents, so look at the management of such incidents and the procedures to be followed
- ensure that all *groups* of employees and others who might be affected are considered – do not forget office staff, night cleaners, maintenance staff, security guards, visitors
- identify *groups of workers who might be particularly at risk*, for example, young or inexperienced workers, those who work alone, any disabled staff
- take account of *existing preventative or precautionary measures* – they may already reduce the risk sufficiently in terms of what needs to be done to comply with the relevant statutory provisions, but are they working properly, does action need to be taken to ensure they are properly maintained?

17 The level of detail in a risk assessment should be broadly proportionate to the risk. The purpose is not to catalogue every trivial hazard; nor is the employer or self-employed person expected to be able to anticipate hazards beyond the limits of current knowledge. A suitable and sufficient risk assessment will reflect what it is reasonably practicable to expect employers to know about the hazards in their workplaces.

18 Where *employees of different employers* work in the same workplace, their respective employers would have to consider risks to their own employees and to the other employer's employees and may have to cooperate to produce an overall risk assessment. Detailed requirements on cooperation and coordination are covered by regulation 9.

19 In some cases, employers may make a first rough assessment, to eliminate from consideration those risks on which no further action need be taken. This should also show where a fuller assessment is needed, if appropriate, using more sophisticated techniques. However, care should be taken not to exaggerate the level of sophistication needed. As mentioned above, the use of quantified risk assessment will be needed only in the most extreme cases, and most of those are already identified by specific regulations.

20 Employers who control a number of *similar workplaces* containing *similar activities* may produce a basic *model risk assessment* reflecting the core hazards and risks associated with these activities. Model assessments may also be developed by trade associations, employers' bodies or other organisations concerned with a particular activity. Such model assessments may be applied by employers or managers at each workplace, but only if they:

- satisfy themselves that the model assessment is broadly appropriate to their type of work
- adapt the model to the detail of their own actual work situations, including any extension necessary to cover hazards and risks not referred to in the model.

Assessment under other regulations

21 Other regulations also contain requirements for risk assessment, but they are addressed specifically to the hazards and risks that are covered by those regulations. An assessment made for the purpose of such regulations will cover in part the obligation to make assessments under these regulations. Where employers have already carried out assessments under other regulations, they need not repeat those assessments so long as they remain valid, but they do need to ensure that all significant risks are covered.

22 Where an employer is assessing a work situation or activity for the first time, a first rough assessment may be particularly useful in identifying those aspects of the work where a more detailed risk assessment may be needed in accordance with other regulations. The *overall risk assessment* under this regulation might then consist of *separate risk assessments* covering particular duties under other regulations, plus a further risk assessment covering any aspects of the work not covered elsewhere.

Recording

23 While all employers and self-employed people are required to make a risk assessment, the regulations also provide that employers with *five or more employees* must record the significant findings of their risk assessment. This record should represent an effective statement of hazards and risks that leads management to take the relevant actions to protect health and safety. It therefore needs to be part of an employer's overall approach to health and safety and, where appropriate, should be linked to other health and safety records, such as the *record of health and safety arrangements* required by regulation 4 and the written *health and safety policy statement* required by section 2(3) of the HSWA.

24 The record would normally be in writing, but it could also be recorded by other means (for instance electronically), so long as it is retrievable for use by management or for examination, say by an inspector or a safety representative. The record will often refer to and rely on other documents and records describing procedures and safeguards. In cases of highly hazardous plant, where by law a *safety case* must be presented, the safety case documents will frequently incorporate the risk assessment so far as the main processes are concerned, and will probably be referred to as an *ancillary document*.

25 The *significant findings* should include:

- the *significant hazards* identified in the assessment, that is, those hazards that might pose serious risk to workers or others who might be affected by the work activity if they were not properly controlled
- the *existing control measures* in place and the extent to which they control the risks (this need not replicate details of measures more fully described in works manuals, etc., but could refer to them)

- the *population* that might be affected by these significant risks or hazards, including any *groups* of employees who are especially at risk.

26 In many cases, employers (or the self-employed) will need to record sufficient detail of the assessment itself, in addition to the significant findings, so that they can demonstrate (to an inspector or safety representatives, for example) that they have undertaken a suitable and sufficient risk assessment and, if circumstances change, the assessment can be readily reviewed and, if necessary, revised. Only in the most straightforward and obvious cases in which the risk assessment can be easily repeated and explained is a record totally unnecessary.

Preventative and protective measures

27 The preventative and protective measures that have to be taken following the risk assessment depend on the relevant legislation – both the HSWA and legislation covering particular hazards or sectors of work – and the risk assessment. In deciding on the measures, employers and the self-employed should apply the following *principles*:

- it is always best, *if possible, to avoid a risk altogether,* for example by not using or stocking a particular dangerous substance or article if it is not essential to the business
- *combat risks at source,* rather than by palliative measures, so if the steps are slippery, say, treating or replacing them is better than providing a warning sign
- *where possible, adapt the work to the individual* – especially as regards the design of workplaces, the choice of work equipment and the choice of working and production methods – with a view, in particular, to alleviating monotonous work and work at a predetermined rate. This helps reduce possible adverse effects on health and safety
- *take advantage of technologial and technical progress,* which often offers opportunities to improve working methods and make them safer

- risk prevention measures need to *form part of a coherent policy and approach,* having the effect of progressively reducing those risks that cannot be prevented or avoided altogether, and take account of the way work is to be organised, working conditions, the working environment and any relevant social factors (health and safety policies required under section 2(3) of the HSWA should be prepared and applied by reference to these principles)
- *give priority to those measures that protect the whole workplace* and all those who work there, thus yielding the greatest benefit, that is, give collective protective measures priority over individual measures
- workers, whether employees or self-employed *need to understand what they need to do*
- the avoidance, prevention and reduction of risks at work needs to be an accepted part of the approach and attitudes at all levels of the organisation and to apply to all its activities, that is, *the existence of an active health and safety culture affecting the organisation as a whole needs to be assured.*

(See further Chapter 3, The risk assessment process.)

Workplace (Health, Safety and Welfare) Regulations 1992

These regulations place a general duty on employers to ensure compliance with any requirement of same. The regulations must be read in conjunction with the general duty to assess risks under the MHSWR in terms of workplace and work activity risk assessment.

Regulation 4

1 Every employer shall ensure that every workplace, modification, extension or conversion under his control and where any of his employees' work complies with any requirements of these regulations that:

   - applies to that workplace or, as the case may be, to the workplace that contains that modification, extension or conversion
   - is in force in respect of that workplace, modification, extension or conversion.

ACOP

17 In some cases, measures additional to those indicated in the regulations and the ACOP may be necessary in order to fully comply with general duties under the HSWA. The MHSWR require employers and self-employed people to assess risks and an associated ACOP states that it is always best, if possible, to avoid a risk altogether and that work should, where possible, be adapted to the individual. A risk assessment may show that the workplace or the work should be reorganised so that the need for people to work, for example, at an unguarded edge or in temperatures that may induce stress, does not arise in the first place.

(See further Chapter 6, Workplace and work activity risk assessments.)

Provision and Use of Work Equipment Regulations 1992

These regulations cover the suitability of work equipment. The duty to assess risks associated with work equipment is implied in the regulations in the following ways.

Regulation 5

1 Every employer shall ensure that work equipment is so constructed or adapted as to be suitable for the purpose for which it is used or provided.

2 In selecting work equipment, every employer shall have regard to the working conditions and to the risks to the health and safety of people that exist on the premises or undertaking in which that work equipment is to be used and any additional risk posed by the use of that work equipment.

3 Every employer shall ensure that work equipment is used only for operations for which, and under the conditions for which, it is suitable.

4 In this regulation, *suitable* means suitable in any respect that it is reasonable to foresee will affect the health or safety of anyone.

HSE Guidance Notes

62 The risk assessment carried out under regulation 3(1) of the MHSWR will help employers to select work equipment and assess its suitability for particular tasks.

(See further Chapter 7, Work equipment risk assessments.)

Personal Protective Equipment at Work Regulations 1992

Under these regulations, an employer must provide *suitable* personal protective equipment (PPE) (regulation 4). An assessment shall be made before choosing any particular PPE along the following lines.

Regulation 6

1 Before choosing any PPE that, by virtue of regulation 4, he is required to ensure is provided, an employer or self-employed person shall ensure that an assessment is made to determine whether or not the equipment he intends will be provided is suitable.

2 The assessment required under paragraph 1 shall include:

- an assessment of any risk or risks to health or safety that have not been avoided by other means
- the definition of the characteristics that PPE must have in order to be effective against the risks referred to in sub-paragraph (a) of this paragraph, taking into account any risks that the equipment itself may create
- comparison with the characteristics of the PPE available with the characteristics referred to in sub-paragraph (b) of this paragraph.

3 Every employer or self-employed person who is required by paragraph 1 to ensure that any assessment is made shall ensure that any such assessment is reviewed if:

- there is reason to suspect that it is no longer valid
- there has been a significant change in the matters to which it relates, and where, as a result of any such review, changes in the

assessment are required, the relevant employer or self-employed person shall ensure that they are made.

HSE Guidance Notes

37 The purpose of the assessment provision in regulation 6 is to ensure that the employer who needs to provide PPE chooses equipment that is correct for the particular risks involved and for the circumstances of its use. It follows from, but does not duplicate, the risk assessment requirements of the MHSWR.

(See further Chapter 8, Personal protective equipment risk assessments.)

Manual Handling Operations Regulations 1992

These regulations place duties on employers where manual handling operations (as defined) are carried out.

1 Each employer shall:

- so far as is reasonably practicable, *avoid* the need for his employees to undertake any manual handling operations at work that involve a risk of their being injured
- where it is not reasonably practicable to avoid the need for his employees to undertake any manual handling operations at work that involve a risk of their being injured:
  - make a suitable and sufficient assessment of all such manual handling operations to be undertaken by them, having regard to the factors that are specified in column 1 of Schedule 1 to these regulations and considering the questions that are specified opposite this in column 2 of that Schedule
  - take appropriate steps to reduce the risk of injury to those employees arising out of their undertaking any such manual handling operations to the lowest level reasonably practicable
  - take appropriate steps to provide any of those employees who are undertaking any such manual handling operations with general indications and, where it is reasonably practicable to do so, precise information on:

- the weight of each load
- the heaviest side of any load whose centre of gravity is not positioned centrally.

2 Any assessment such as is referred to in paragraph (1)(b)(i) of this regulation shall be reviewed by the employer who made it if:

- there is reason to suspect it is no longer valid
- there has been a significant change in the manual handling operations to which it relates

and where, as a result of any such review, changes to an assessment are required, the relevant employer shall make them.

HSE Guidance Notes

The HSE Guidance Notes accompanying the regulations go into considerable depth regarding the question of manual handling risk assessments.

33 Where the general assessment carried out under regulation 3(1) of the MHSWR indicates a possibility of injury from manual handling operations but the conclusion reached under regulation 4(1)(a) is that avoidance of the operations is not reasonably practicable, a more specific assessment should be carried out as required by regulation 4(1)(b)(i). The extent to which this further assessment needs to be pursued will depend on the circumstances. Appendix 1 offers some simple numerical guidelines to assist with this decision. The guidelines are intended to be used as an initial filter, to help to identify those operations deserving more detailed assessment.

34 Schedule 1 to the regulations specifies factors that the assessment should take into account including the *task, load, working environment* and *individual capability.*

(See further Chapter 9, Manual handling risk assessments.)

Health and Safety (Display Screen Equipment) Regulations 1992

These regulations require an employer to undertake workstation *analysis* in order to reduce risks to display screen equipment users.

Regulation 2

Regulation 2 is framed thus.

1 Every employer shall perform a suitable and sufficient analysis of those workstations that:

- (regardless of who has provided them) are used for the purposes of his undertaking by *users*
- have been provided by him and are used for the purposes of his undertaking by *operators*

for the purpose of assessing the health and safety risks to which those people are exposed in consequence of that use.

2 Any assessment made by an employer in pursuance of paragraph (1) shall be reviewed by him if:

- there is reason to suspect that it is no longer valid
- there has been a significant change in the matters to which it relates

and where, as a result of any such review, changes to an assessment are required, the employer concerned shall make them.

3 The employer shall reduce the risks in consequence of an assessment to the lowest extent reasonably practicable.

4 The reference in paragraph (3) to 'an assessment' is a reference to an assessment made by the employer concerned in pursuance of paragraph (1) and changed by him where necessary in pursuance of paragraph (2).

Users and operators

These two terms are significant in terms of the application of the regulations to an organisation's display screen equipment operations.

A *user* means an **employee** who *habitually* uses display screen equipment as a *significant* part of his *normal* work.

An *operator* means a **self-employed person** who *habitually* uses display screen equipment as a *significant* part of his *normal* work.

In both cases, the terms 'habitually', 'significant' and 'normal' are important in determining the need for workstation risk analysis. A substantial number of people use display screen equipment, or have access to same, at work but may not necessarily be classified as 'users' or 'operators' under the regulations. The Guidance Notes issued with the regulations clarify this situation.

HSE Guidance Notes

12 In some cases, it will be clear that use of display screen equipment is more or less continuous on most days and the individuals concerned should be regarded as users or operators. This will include the majority of those whose job mainly involves, for example, display screen-based data input or sales and order processing. Where use is less continuous or frequent, other factors connected with the job must be assessed. It will generally be appropriate to classify the person concerned as a user or operator if most or all of the following criteria apply:

- the individual *depends* on the use of display screen equipment to do the job, as alternative means for achieving the same results are not readily available
- the individual has *no discretion* as to use or non-use of the display screen equipment
- the individual needs *significant training and/or particular skills* in the use of display screen equipment to do the job
- the individual normally uses display screen equipment for *continuous spells of an hour or more at a time*
- the individual uses display screen equipment in this way *more or less daily*
- *fast transfer of information between the user and screen* is an important requirement of the job
- the performance requirements of the system demand *high levels of attention and concentration by the user*, for example, where the consequences of error may be critical.

Various examples of display screen equipment users are given in the Guidance Notes to the regulations.

The Guidance Notes issued with the regulations cover what is a suitable and sufficient analysis and risk assessment, the form of the assessment, situations relating to shared workstations, assessment of risks to homeworkers, who should do assessments, the review of assessments, measures necessary to reduce risks, sources of information and advice, and standards.

Annex B: Display screen equipment: possible effects on health

This deals with the main hazards associated with the use of display screen equipment.

20 Employers will need to assess the extent to which any of the risks (summarised at Annex B) arise for display screen equipment workers using their workstations who are:

- users employed by them
- users employed by others (such as agency employed temps)
- operators, that is, self-employed contractors who would be classified as users if they were employees (such as self-employed agency temps, self-employed journalists).

Individual workstations used by any of these people will need to be analysed and any risks assessed. If employers require their employees to use workstations at home, these, too, will need to be assessed.

If there is any doubt as to whether any individual is a user or operator, carrying out a risk assessment should help in reaching a decision.

(See further Chapter 10, Display screen equipment risk analyses.)

Noise at Work Regulations 1989

Under these regulations, there is a general duty on employers to reduce the risk of damage to the hearing of employees from exposure to noise to the lowest level reasonably practicable (regulation 6). The regulations further place an absolute duty on an employer to ensure noise assessments are carried out in certain circumstances.

The regulations define three *action levels*:

- the *first action level* means a daily personal noise exposure of 85 decibels(A)
- the *peak action level* means a level of peak sound pressure of 200 pascals

- the *second action level* means a daily personal noise exposure of 90 decibels(A).

Regulation 4

1 Every employer shall, when any of his employees is *likely* to be exposed to the first action level (85 decibels(A)) or above to the peak action level (200 pascals) or above, ensure that a competent person makes a noise assessment that is adequate for the purposes:
   - of identifying which of his employees are so exposed
   - of providing him with such information with regard to the noise to which those employees may be exposed as will facilitate compliance with his duties under regulations 7 (reduction of noise exposure), 8 (ear protection), 9 (ear protection zones) and 11 (provision of information to employees).

2 The noise assessment required by paragraph 1 shall be reviewed when:
   - there is reason to suspect that the assessment is no longer valid
   - there has been a significant change in the work to which the assessment relates

   and where, as a result of the review, changes in the assessment are required, those changes shall be made.

HSE Guidance Notes

The purpose of assessment

21 Regulation 4(1) requires an employer to arrange for a noise assessment whenever an employee is likely to be exposed to or above the first or the peak action level. The assessment will need to:
   - identify all workers likely to be exposed
   - provide enough information to enable appropriate action to be taken.

Deciding whether or not an assessment is needed

22 A preliminary decision on whether or not an assessment is needed can usually be reached without making detailed noise measurements.

23 As a rough guide, an assessment of daily personal noise exposure will usually be needed wherever people have to shout or have difficulty being heard clearly by someone about 2 metres away or if they find it difficult to talk to each other. Where there is any doubt, some measurements of the noise should be taken in a few representative places. If this suggests that any workers might be exposed to the first action level or more, it will be necessary to go on to a more comprehensive assessment.

24 Assessments of *peak pressure* are most likely to be needed where workers are exposed to loud noises from explosive sources, such as cartridge-operated tools or detonators. They might also be needed where there are high levels of impact noise.

The assessment

25 An assessment will be adequate if it meets the objectives set out above. It will need to be based on reliable information about work patterns and noise levels, so the affected employees and their safety representatives should be consulted; this will also help ensure their cooperation in any control measures that might turn out to be needed.

26 An *adequate assessment* can usually be made without making a detailed measurement of each worker's exposure, for example:

- where groups of workers are employed in an area throughout which the noise level is reasonably uniform, the assessment might be based on noise levels measured in the working area and the length of time that workers are likely to spend there
- where groups of workers perform similar tasks, sample measurements on a group or activity basis might be adequate, provided that it is representative of individuals within the group
- sometimes a calculated exposure will be adequate if sufficient information is available about the noise the machines produce during operation, and the nature and duration of tasks carried out by the workers (for example, where workers use noisy hand tools, it may be possible to measure the noise level in typical jobs and assess the exposure produced by different patterns of use).

27 Detailed advice on noise surveys is given in *Noise Guide No. 3: Equipment and procedures for noise surveys*.

Variable exposure to noise

28 Some workers are exposed to noise levels that vary considerably either during the day or from one day to another, because, for example, they visit a number of noisy areas or do a variety of jobs requiring intermittent use of noisy tools and machines. Sometimes it will be impracticable or of little use to make an accurate measurement of daily personal noise exposure for these workers.

29 In these circumstances, the best course will usually be to treat all working areas where the average noise level (or *equivalent continuous sound level*) is 85 or 90 decibels (A) or more as places where the corresponding action levels are likely to be exceeded until a better assessment can be made.

Review of assessments

30 The assessments will need to be kept up to date. After the employer has made his initial decision on the action required under the regulations, information will continue to be needed to allow him to keep his noise control and PPE programmes under review. Similarly, where practical difficulties limit the information that can be obtained (for example, as described in paragraph 28), developments in assessment procedures and equipment might later mean that a more detailed assessment can be made. The assessment should be reviewed whenever there are any significant changes in equipment or the work or any other reason exists that suggest it is no longer valid.

31 Changes that might create the need for a review include:

- installation or removal of machinery
- substantial changes in workload, work pattern or machine speeds
- changes in building structure or machine layout
- machine wear or general deterioration

- modifications to machinery and introduction of automation
- the noise control programme.

32 Even where there have been no obvious changes, workplaces should not be left for long periods without checking to discover whether or not there is, in fact, any need for a review (for example, because of a gradual increase in noise level due to machine wear). Spot checks can be made by establishing a few selected locations where the noise is measured periodically, such as places where exposure is high or a gradual increase is likely. The intervals between checks will depend on local circumstances, but, for most kinds of machinery, the maximum would be about two years.

Competent persons

33 The assessments have to be made by a competent person. The employer will need to make sure that the work is done by someone able to produce an assessment meeting the objectives in paragraph 21. The competent person will not have to make all noise measurements personally – often he or she will be able to supervise collection of information on noise levels and exposure and its use in the final assessment.

1

34 The competent person will need to be capable of not only measuring noise, but of bringing together and presenting enough information about the noise exposure to enable the employer to make correct decisions on what should be done to comply with the regulations or of advising whether or not additional specialist support is needed. *Knowledge* alone will not be sufficient; the person should possess *experience* and *skill* appropriate to the situations to be handled. The skills and knowledge needed will include:

- the purpose of the assessments
- an appreciation of his or her own limitations, whether they be in terms of knowledge, experience, facilities or resources
- how to record results and explain them to others
- the reasons for using various kinds of instruments and their limitations

- how to interpret information provided by others – for example on the noise generated by tools and the jobs done with them – to calculate probable exposures.

35 The level of expertise needed will depend largely on the complexity of the situation to be assessed. Where workers are regularly exposed to steady noise throughout the working day (for example, in a weaving shed) or to intermittent but regular periods of steady noise, the task is straightforward and little beyond the ability to handle simple instruments and relate their readings to the requirements of the regulations will be needed. Those who are to assess irregular exposures or situations where workers intermittently use a variety of different machines, will need a better understanding of techniques.

36 The ability to understand and apply the HSE's Guidance Notes in order to make an assessment meeting the objectives in paragraph 21 is more important than formal qualifications. Many engineers, scientists and other technical staff will have gained sufficient skill to carry out a competent assessment through practical experience of making noise measurements and using the results. Some will, however, need further training. This may be available through short courses provided by technical colleges and other institutions. Advice on training is given in *Noise Guide No. 6: Training for competent persons*.

(See further Chapter 5, Noise risk assessments.)

Control of Substances Hazardous to Health Regulations 1994

The COSHH regulations place an absolute duty on an employer, where employees are liable to be exposed to substances hazardous to health, to make a health risk assessment of the risks created by that work.

Regulation 6

1 Any employer shall not carry out any work that is liable to expose any employees to any substance hazardous to health unless he has

made a suitable and sufficient assessment of the risks created by that work to the health of those employees and of the steps that need to be taken to meet the requirements of these regulations.

2 The assessment required by paragraph 1 shall be reviewed regularly and forthwith if:

- there is reason to suspect that the assessment is no longer valid
- there has been a significant change in the work to which the risk assessment relates

and where, as a result of the review, changes in the assessment are required, those changes shall be made.

General ACOP

The subject of health risk assessment is dealt with in considerable depth in this ACOP.

12 The purpose of an assessment is to enable a valid decision to be made about measures necessary to control substances hazardous to health arising from any work. It also enables the employer to demonstrate readily, both to himself and others, that all the factors pertinent to the work have been considered and that an informed and valid judgement has been reached about the risks, the steps that need to be taken to achieve and maintain adequate control, the need for monitoring exposure at the workplace and the need for health surveillance.

1

13 Whoever carries out the assessment should be competent to do so in accordance with regulation 12(3).

Suitable and sufficient

14 A *suitable and sufficient* assessment should include:

- an assessment of the risks to health
- consideration of the practicability of preventing exposure to hazardous substances
- the steps that need to be taken to achieve adequate control of exposure where prevention is not reasonably practicable, in accordance with regulation 7

- identification of other action necessary to comply with regulations 8–12.

15 An assessment of the risks created by any work should involve:

- consideration of:
  - which *substances or types of substance* (including biological agents) employees are liable to be exposed to (taking into account the consequences of possible failure of any control measure provided to meet the requirements of regulation 7)
  - what *effects* those substances can have on the body
  - where the substances are likely to be *present* and in what *form*
  - the ways in which, and the extent to which, *any groups of employees or other people* could potentially be *exposed*, taking into account the nature of the work and process and any reasonably foreseeable deterioration in, or failure of, any control measures provided for the purposes of regulation 7
- an estimate of *exposure*, taking into account engineering measures and systems of work currently employed for controlling potential exposure
- where *valid standards* exist, representing adequate control, comparison of the estimate with those standards.

16 If comparison shows that control is likely to be inadequate or become inadequate, then the assessment should go on to determine the steps or, in the case of existing work, the further steps that need to be taken to obtain and sustain adequate control. As required by regulation 7, PPE should only be considered as a method of control after all other measures have been taken, so far as is reasonably practicable.

17 An assessment can be considered suitable and sufficient if the detail and expertise with which it is carried out are commensurate with the nature and degree of risk arising from the work, as well as the complexity and variability of the process.

18 The amount of detailed work involved in carrying out a suitable and sufficient risk assessment will vary and will depend on the extent to which:

- the degree and nature of the risk and conclusions about the adequacy of proposed or existing control measures are immediately obvious

- knowledge has already been gained as a result of previous experience
- existing records are valid, concerning the nature of the substances involved, the numbers and categories of employees potentially exposed, their work activities, the results of exposure experienced hitherto and the suitability of existing methods of control.

19 In some circumstances, it will only be necessary to read suppliers' information sheets to conclude that existing practices are sufficient to ensure adequate control of exposure. In others, it may be necessary to read the HSE's Guidance Notes, manufacturers' standards, technical papers or trade literature to estimate the likely exposure before deciding what control measures should be applied.

20 The assessment may necessitate the carrying out of atmospheric sampling and measurement to determine exposure, particularly where operations are complicated or specialised and the substances involved have an *occupational exposure limit*.

Provision of information

21 In the simplest and most obvious cases, which can be easily repeated and explained at any time, an assessment need not be recorded. However, in most cases, to be suitable and sufficient, it will need to be recorded and kept readily accessible to ensure continuity and accuracy of knowledge among all those who may need to know the results.

22 Employees or their representatives at the place of work should be informed of the results of the assessment in accordance with regulation 12(1).

Review of assessment

23 The assessment should be reviewed regularly and, in any case, whenever there is evidence to suspect that it is no longer valid or where there has been a significant change in the work to which the assessment relates.

24 The assessment may be shown to be no longer valid because of, for example:

- the results of periodic thorough examinations and tests of engineering controls (regulation 9)
- the results of monitoring exposure at the workplace (regulation 10)
- the results of health surveillance (regulation 11) or a confirmed case of occupationally induced disease
- new information on health risks.

25 A significant change in the work may be:

- in the substances used or their source
- plant modification, including engineering controls
- in the process or methods of work
- in the volume or rate of production.

26 Arrangements should be made to ensure that the assessment is reviewed regularly. The assessment should include a *decision* and, where the assessment is written, a *statement*, specifying the maximum period that should elapse between the date of the initial assessment and the date of the first review, and then between successive reviews. The length of the period chosen will depend on the nature of the risk, the work and a judgement on the likelihood of changes occurring, but, in any case, the assessment should be reviewed at least every five years.

27 Reviews triggered by these arrangements will provide the opportunity to reconsider the practicability of preventing exposure to hazardous substances by changes to the process or by the use of less hazardous substances. This might now be practicable because of technological changes or because of changes in the relationship between costs of substances, equipment used and control measures since the last assessment. Similarly, control measures should be re-examined to assess the feasibility of further improvement – for example, where substances with MELs are involved, do the controls really reduce exposure as far as is reasonably practicable or merely below the MELs?

(See further Chapter 4, Health risk assessments.)

CONCLUSION

The law on risk assessment is very broad in some respects, but the basic principles, as indicated in the ACOP to the MHSWR, will always apply.

Clearly, no two people assess risk in the same way, let alone attempt to quantify it in the same way. To comply with the regulations, organisations need to establish and implement some form of assessment procedure that will be acceptable in a court and which takes into account the legal principles involved. Furthermore, the system for measuring and evaluating risk should be acceptable to all parties concerned – employers, employees, contractors, officers of the enforcement agencies and, perhaps, insurers.

Principal areas of health and safety management

Regulation 3 of the MHSWR requires every employer to make a *suitable and sufficient assessment* of:

- the risks to the health and safety of his employees to which they are exposed while at work
- the risks to the health and safety of people not in his employment arising out of or in connection with the conduct by him of his undertaking

for the purpose of identifying the measures he needs to take to comply with the *requirements and prohibitions* imposed on him by or under the *relevant statutory provisions*.

Regulation 4 of these regulations places an absolute duty on an employer to make and give effect to such arrangements as are appropriate, having regard to the nature of his activities and the size of his undertaking, for the effective *planning, organisation, control, monitoring and review of the preventive and protective measures*.

Compliance with both these requirements should, therefore, follow a number of stages.

STAGES OF THE MANAGEMENT OPERATION

1 Identify the hazards through various forms of safety monitoring.

2 Identify the risks, and the extent of the risks, from the identified hazards by a form of risk assessment, taking into account current preventative and protective strategies.

3 Identify those *relevant statutory provisions* that apply to the organisation's operations and the *requirements and prohibitions* imposed by these provisions.

4 Recorded risk assessments, whether generic or specific, should identify actions required on short-term, medium-term and long-term bases.

5 Decide whether a *prevention* or *protection strategy* is appropriate for the identified risks people are neither prevented or protected against exposure to.

6 Implement the recommendations arising from risk assessments on a phased basis over the next five years, taking into account human capability.

7 Monitor and review the performance of staff and others in complying with strategies introduced to prevent or protect against exposure to identified risks.

8 At all stages, ensure health and safety information, instruction and training is provided to those affected, including non-employees.

THE INTEGRATED APPROACH TO HEALTH AND SAFETY MANAGEMENT

The risk assessment, undertaken on a regular basis, forms the basis for future health and safety management systems and procedures. These can include:

1 safety monitoring systems, such as safety audits, safety inspections, safety sampling exercises, safety tours and health and safety reviews

2 training and regular retraining of appointed competent persons

3 the introduction and operation of:

- planned preventative maintenance schemes for workplaces and work equipment
- cleaning programmes

- emergency procedures
- health surveillance of certain groups of staff
- procedures for regulating the activities of contractors, such as contractors' regulations
- procedures for ensuring the health and safety of staff working away from base, for example, rent collectors or housing maintenance staff
- procedures for ensuring the giving of health and safety information, instruction and training for all staff
- human capability assessment
- specific joint consultation procedures.

4 The formal documentation of safe systems of work.

5 The production of in-house codes of practice and guidance notes to ensure consistency of approach by managers.

6 To raise the profile of health and safety, there is a case for implementing various forms of award system to recognise high standards of performance.

7 Above all, health and safety must be seen to be an integral feature of the management system and so the achievement of performance levels should be recognised in the reward structure of the organisation. All levels of management must be aware of their responsibilities for health and safety at work. Health and safety performance objectives, which are measurable and achievable by the staff concerned, should be agreed on a regular basis and performance measured against these agreed objectives.

THE STATEMENT OF HEALTH AND SAFETY POLICY

This document is the starting point for all health and safety management systems and its relevance must be appreciated by all levels of the organisation. Far too many statements of health and safety policy are inadequate in that they do not indicate, for instance, a clear hierarchy of responsibility for health and safety from the top level of management to individual employee level, the hazards and precautions arising from the business activities, the legislation that applies to the business or the systems for monitoring health and safety performance.

A policy statement should incorporate the following three parts.

- *Part 1: General statement of intent* (specifying objectives)

This part should outline the organisation's overall philosophy in relation to the management of health and safety.

- *Part 2: Organisation* (People and their duties)

This part should show clearly who is responsible to whom and for what – the chain of command (a management structure diagram is useful in this respect). Part 2 should demonstrate how accountabilities are fixed, how policy documentation is to be monitored, how joint consultation will function and how individual job descriptions should reflect health and safety responsibilities and associated accountabilities.

- *Part 3: Arrangements* (systems and procedures)

This part should detail the practical arrangements in force to assist in overall policy implementation. These include, for instance, the systems and procedures for safety training, safety monitoring, accident reporting and investigation, operation of safe systems of work, risk assessment and emergency procedures.

ANNUAL HEALTH AND SAFETY PLANS

Many organisations produce a formal health and safety plan, which incorporates clearly identifiable and achievable objectives for managers in a number of areas of health and safety at work. Such objectives or targets could be linked to, for example, the completion of risk assessments, the implementation of defined safe systems of work, the development and implementation of training programmes and the introduction of systems for ensuring safe contracting operations.

RISK ASSESSMENTS

Risk assessment is an integral feature of health and safety management and includes the development and implementation of risk assessment methodology in connection with workplaces, work activities and the more specific forms of risk assessment required in the case of manual handling operations, display screen equipment and the use of PPE (see further chapters 3–10).

SAFETY MONITORING OPERATIONS

Far too many organisations rely on feedback from accidents and work-induced ill health as a measure of health and safety performance. In many cases, this form of reactive approach does not identify the real problems and their causes, both direct and indirect. Proactive monitoring systems – such as the undertaking of regular safety inspections, audits and tours – will provide a far better indication of continuing levels of health and safety performance.

COMPETENT PERSONS

The expression 'competent person' occurs frequently in construction safety legislation. For example, under the Construction (General Provisions) Regulations 1961 and the Construction (Working Places) Regulations 1966, certain inspections, examinations, operations and supervisory duties must be undertaken by such persons. What a 'competent person' is, however, is not generally defined in law, except in the Electricity at Work Regulations 1989 and the Pressure Systems and Transportable Gas Containers Regulations 1989. Therefore, the onus is on the employer to decide whether or not those they employ or contract are competent to carry out these duties. An employer might do this by reference to the person's training, qualifications and experience. Broadly, a competent person should have practical and theoretical knowledge as well as sufficient experience of the particular machinery, plant or procedure involved to enable him to identify defects or weaknesses during plant and machinery examinations and to assess their importance in relation to the strength and function of that plant and machinery. He must be able to discover defects and determine the consequences of such defects (*Brazier* v. *Skipton Rock Co. Ltd* (1962) 1 AER 955).

Competent persons are involved in many activities, including:

- supervision of demolition work
- supervision of the handling and use of explosives
- inspection of scaffold materials prior to erection
- supervision of erection of, substantial alterations or additions to, and dismantling of scaffolds
- inspection of scaffolds every seven days and after adverse weather conditions that could affect the strength and stability of a scaffold, or cause displacement of any part
- inspection of excavations on a daily basis
- supervision of the erection of cranes
- testing of cranes after erection, re-erections and any removal or adjustment involving change of anchorage or ballasting
- examination of appliances for anchorage or ballasting prior to erection.

Competent persons and the MHSWR

Under regulation 6, every employer shall appoint one or more competent persons to assist him in undertaking the measures he needs to take to comply with the requirements and prohibitions imposed on him by or under the relevant statutory provisions (regulation 6(1)).

But what are the 'relevant statutory provisions'? These include the HSWA (the statute) and all the regulations made under the HSWA, which must be taken into account in a risk assessment and may be relevant to the employer's activities.

Regulation 6(5) states that a person shall be regarded as competent for the purposes of paragraph (1) where he has sufficient training and experience or knowledge and other qualities to enable him properly to assist in undertaking the measures referred to in that paragraph.

The ACOP makes the following points with regard to competent persons.

> Employers may appoint one or more of their employees to do all that is necessary or may enlist help or support from outside the organisation, or they may do both. Employers who are sole traders, or are members of a partnership, may appoint themselves (or other partners) to carry out health and safety measures, so long as they are competent. Large employers may well appoint a whole department with specific health and safety responsibilities, including specialists in such matters as occupational hygiene or safety engineering. In any case, where external support is brought in, its activities must be coordinated by those appointed by the employer to manage the health and safety measures.
>
> External services employed usually will be appointed in an advisory capacity only. They will often be specialists or general consultants on health and safety matters.
>
> The appointment of such health and safety assistants, departments or advisers does not absolve the employer from responsibilities for health and safety under the HSWA and other relevant statutory provisions. It can do no more than give added assurance that these responsibilities will be discharged adequately.
>
> Employers are solely responsible for ensuring that those they appoint to assist them with health and safety measures are competent to carry out whatever tasks they are assigned and given adequate information and support. In making their decisions, employers should take into account the need for:
>
> (a) a knowledge and understanding of the work involved, the principles of risk assessment and prevention, and current health and safety applications;
>
> (b) the capacity to apply this to the task required by the employer which might include identifying the health and safety problems, assessing the need for action, designing and developing strategy and plans, evaluating their effectiveness and promoting and communicating health and safety and welfare advances and practices.
>
> Competence in the sense it is used in these Regulations does not necessarily depend on the possession of particular skills or qualifications. Simple situations may require only the following:
>
> (a) an understanding of relevant current best practice;
>
> (b) awareness of the limitations of one's own experience and knowledge; and

(c) the willingness and ability to supplement existing experience and knowledge.

The provision of effective health and safety measures in more complex or highly technical situations will call for specific applied knowledge and skills which can be offered by appropriately qualified specialists. In the case of specific knowledge and skills in occupational health and safety, membership of a professional body or similar organisation at an appropriate level and in an appropriate part of health and safety, or possession of an appropriate qualification in health and safety, can help guide employers. Competence-based qualifications accredited by the National Council for Vocational Qualifications and SCOTVEC (the Scottish Vocational Education Council), which are being developed for most occupations, may also provide a guide.

PLANNED PREVENTATIVE MAINTENANCE SCHEMES

Regulation 5 of the Workplace (Health, Safety and Welfare) Regulations 1992 places an absolute duty on employers to operate some form of planned preventative maintenance in the following ways.

1 The workplace and the equipment, devices and systems to which this regulation applies shall be maintained (including cleaning as appropriate) in *an efficient state, in efficient working order and in good repair*.

2 Where appropriate, the equipment, devices and systems to which this regulation applies shall be subject to a *suitable system of maintenance*.

3 The *equipment, devices and systems* to which this regulation applies are:

   - equipment and devices in which a fault is liable to result in a failure to comply with any of these regulations
   - mechanical ventilation systems provided pursuant to regulation 6 (whether or not they include equipment or devices within sub-paragraph (a) of this paragraph).

Similar provisions apply in the case of work equipment, defined as 'any machinery, appliance, apparatus or tool or any assembly of components which, in order to achieve a common end, are arranged and controlled so that they function as a whole'. Regulation 6 of the Provision and Use of Work Equipment Regulations 1992 places a further absolute duty on employers:

- every employer shall ensure that work equipment is maintained in *an efficient state, in efficient working order and in good repair*
- every employer shall ensure that where any *machinery* has a *maintenance log*, the log is kept up to date.

Quite clearly, the duty to operate planned preventative maintenance systems is manifest in these regulations and failure to show clear evidence of their operation constitutes a breach of them. This implies formal documentation of the system, the provision of information, instruction and training to all those involved in maintenance and regular reviews of the system to ensure its continuing effectiveness.

PURCHASING ARRANGEMENTS

The duties of:

- designers, manufacturers, importers and suppliers of articles for use at work
- erectors or installers of articles for use at work
- manufacturers, importers or suppliers of substances for use at work,

under section 6 of the HSWA are well established. They must ensure, so far as is reasonably practicable, that the design and construction of articles are safe and without risks to health when properly used, the provision of adequate information and, in appropriate cases, the undertaking of research, testing and examination.

Those involved in the purchasing function should be aware of these duties and any contracts for supply, erection or installation should be framed around them. Moreover, current purchasing arrangements may need to be reviewed in the light of information derived from a risk assessment carried out under the MHSWR or other regulations.

PERFORMANCE REVIEW PROCEDURES

Performance review is an important feature of the management process. For instance, reviews of financial and production performance are commonly carried out by most organisations. Reviews of health and safety performance, however, are rare and there is a need for a clearly defined performance review procedure in this field in order to comply with current legislation.

One method of reviewing performance is through the *health and safety review* procedure shown in Figure 2.1. In this system, a number of general and specific aspects of performance are established, such as the level of compliance with a planned preventative maintenance programme, safe system of work and specific chemical handling procedures. Each aspect is ranked on a points scale (from 1 to 5, 1 to 10, etc.) according to the risks involved and its relative significance from a health and safety viewpoint. The individual undertaking the health and safety review scores these various aspects of performance and arrives at a final points total. This produces an indication of the level of compliance and is a useful system for comparing performance across individual workplaces undertaking similar activities, such as engineering workshops, transport maintenance workshops, laboratories, offices, distribution depots and retail premises.

Such a system also enables the early identification of risks that may be common to a group of premises and work activities for which generic risk assessments can be undertaken subsequently.

HUMAN CAPABILITY

Regulation 11(1) of the MHSWR places an absolute duty on employers to assess human capability:

> Every employer shall, in entrusting tasks to his employees, take into account their capabilities as regards health and safety.

This requirement raises a number of important considerations with regard to both physical capability and mental capability. Do all employees possess the physical capability to engage in certain manual

HEALTH AND SAFETY REVIEW	Max	Score	
Workplace			
1 Cleaning and housekeeping	10		
2 Machinery safety	20		
3 Fire protection	20		
4 Electrical safety	10		
5 Structural safety	10		
6 Chemical safety	10		
7 Internal storage	10		
8 Internal transport	10		
Maximum	100		Total
Management systems			
1 Policy statement	10		
2 Risk assessments	10		
3 Competent persons	10		
4 Safe systems of work	20		
5 Hazard reporting	10		
6 Information, instruction, training	10		
7 Accident/Sickness reporting	10		
8 Cleaning schedules	10		
9 Planned maintenance system	10		
Maximum	100		Total
People			
1 Safe behaviour/awareness	40		
2 Personal protection	20		
3 Manual handling	20		
4 Chemical handling	10		
5 Personal hygiene	10		
Maximum	100		Total
Environment			
1 Temperature control	10		
2 Lighting	10		
3 Ventilation	20		
4 Noise control	10		
5 Waste storage and disposal	10		
6 Internal pollution control	10		
7 External pollution control	10		
8 Welfare amenity provisions	20		
Maximum	100		Total
Grand maximum	400		Grand total

FIG 2.1 Example of a health and safety review form

handling operations, such as loading sacks of cement on to pallets or lifting patients in and out of bed? And what about mental capability? Does the average employee understand the chemical and toxicological information contained in the average safety data sheet supplied with a hazardous substance?

The ACOP to the regulations provides extremely limited advice to employers:

> When allocating work to employees, employers should ensure that the demands of the job do not exceed the employees' ability to carry out the work without risks to themselves or others. Employers should take account of the employees' capabilities and the level of their training, knowledge and experience. If additional training is needed, it should be provided.

The question of human capability features strongly in certain areas of the risk assessment process and, in some cases, it may be necessary to restrict certain employees from certain tasks until they show evidence of having understood the messages conveyed to them during their training and instruction. In certain cases, an occupational physician or occupational health nurse may have to make a decision as to an individual's capability to undertake certain tasks of a physical nature.

EMERGENCY PROCEDURES

Emergency procedures in respect of fire are well established under current fire safety legislation, namely the Fire Precautions Act 1971 and the Fire Safety and Safety of Places of Sport Act 1987. However, other emergency procedures may be necessary, for instance, following an environmental pollution incident or where a manufacturing process goes out of control as a result of equipment or instrument failure. The development of an emergency procedure may be one of the significant outcomes of the risk assessment process.

Regulation 7(1) of the MHSWR refers to 'procedures for serious and imminent danger and for danger areas':

> Every employer shall:
>
> (a) establish and where necessary give effect to appropriate procedures to

be followed in the event of serious or imminent danger to persons at work in his undertaking;

(b) nominate a sufficient number of *competent persons* to implement those procedures in so far as they relate to the evacuation from premises of persons at work in his undertaking; and

(c) ensure that none of his employees has access to any area occupied by him to which it is necessary to restrict access on grounds of health and safety unless the employee concerned has received adequate health and safety instruction.

A 'suitable and sufficient' risk assessment should, therefore, identify situations where there is a potential for 'serious and imminent danger'. The employer must then prepare an emergency procedure and nominate competent persons to deal with the evacuation process in the event of an emergency arising. Furthermore, in addition to providing routine fire training for employees and others, such as contractors' employees, it is necessary to instruct those concerned in the more specific emergency procedure prior to their being allowed to work in that area or at a particular activity.

SAFE SYSTEMS OF WORK

A safe system of work is defined as 'the integration of personnel, articles and substances in a suitable environment and workplace to produce an acceptable standard of health and safety. Due consideration must be given to foreseeable emergencies and the provision of adequate rescue facilities'.

The formal preparation of safe systems of work is one of the outcomes of risk assessment. Personnel must be instructed, trained and supervised in the operation of identified safe systems of work.

METHOD STATEMENTS

Method statements are commonly used during construction and related activities and are often derived from risk assessments that have been undertaken.

A method statement is a formally written safe system of work agreed between an occupier/client and contractor or between a main contractor and subcontractor where hazardous work has to be undertaken. It should specify the operations to be carried out on a stage-by-stage basis and indicate the precautions necessary to protect site operators, staff occupying the premises where the work is undertaken and members of the public, including local residents, who may be affected by the work. It may incorporate information and specific requirements stipulated by health and safety practitioners, enforcement officers, the police, site surveyors and the manufacturers and suppliers of plant and equipment or substances used at work. In certain cases, it may identify training needs or the use of specifically trained operators.

Method statements may be necessary to ensure safe systems of work in activities involving:

- the use of substances hazardous to health
- the use of explosives
- lifting operations
- potential fire risk situations
- electrical hazards
- the use of sealed sources of radiation
- the risk of dust explosions or inhalation of toxic dusts
- certain types of excavation adjacent to existing buildings
- demolition operations
- the removal of asbestos from existing buildings.

Contents of a method statement

The following features should be incorporated in a method statement:

- the technique(s) to be used
- access provisions
- safeguarding of existing work locations
- structural stability requirements

- safety of others, including members of the public and local residents
- health precautions, including the use of PPE
- the plant and equipment to be used
- procedures for prevention of area pollution
- segregation of certain areas
- procedures for disposal of toxic wastes
- procedures to ensure compliance with specific legislation, such as the COSHH and Control of Asbestos at Work Regulations 1987.

Asbestos

In addition to the above requirements, the following features should be incorporated in a method statement where work involves the removal, stripping and disposal of asbestos from a building:

- the specific safe system of work to be followed
- procedures for segregation of the asbestos stripping area
- PPE requirements
- welfare amenity provisions, such as hand washing and showers, sanitation arrangements, separation of protective clothing area from personal clothing area, catering facilities, drinking water provision
- ventilation requirements for the working area
- personal hygiene requirements for operators
- supervision arrangements
- air monitoring procedures, including immediate action to be taken on the receipt of unsatisfactory results
- notification requirements under the Control of Asbestos at Work Regulations 1987.

The need for method statements

The need for contractors to produce method statements prior to high-risk operations should be raised in any pre-contract discussion between occupier/client and the main contractor. In certain cases, such as the removal of asbestos, standard forms of method statement are used and signed by the main contractor as an indication of his intent to follow the particular safe system of work agreed between occupier/client and himself.

Under the Construction (Design and Management) Regulations 1994, the procedure for producing and implementing method statements should be incorporated in the health and safety plan required under the regulations. Furthermore, the planning supervisor and principal contractor, appointed in accordance with the regulations, should both be familiar with the procedures for method statements and competent to ensure their implementation. Method statements should be incorporated in the health and safety file held by the client.

HEALTH SURVEILLANCE

Health surveillance is the regular review of the health of employees exposed to various forms of health risk, for instance from hazardous substances or as a result of working on specific processes.

While there is a general duty on an employer under section 2(1) of the HSWA 'to ensure, so far as is reasonably practicable, the *health*, safety and welfare at work of all his employees', more specific duties to provide these can be found in regulations made under the Act, such as the COSHH regulations 1994 and, more recently, the MHSWR.

COSHH regulations 1994

Under regulation 11, 'health surveillance' is defined simply as 'including biological monitoring'. Regulation 11 is framed in the following way:

1 where it is appropriate for the protection of the health of his employees who are, or are liable to be, exposed to a substance hazardous to health, the employer shall ensure that such employees are under suitable health surveillance
2 health surveillance shall be treated as being appropriate where:

- the employee is exposed to one of the substances specified in column 1 of Schedule 5 (such as vinyl chloride monomer (VCM)) and is engaged in a process specified in column 2 of that Schedule (for example, the manufacture of VCM), unless that exposure is not significant
- the exposure of the employee to a substance hazardous to health is such that an identifiable disease or adverse health effect may be related to the exposure, there is a reasonable likelihood that the disease or effect may occur under the particular conditions of his work and there are valid techniques for detecting indications of the disease or the effect.

In the latter case, a typical identifiable disease is dermatitis, occasionally encountered among operators in many industries through exposure to detergents, solvents and oils (see further Chapter 4, Health risk assessments).

Management of Health and Safety at Work Regulations 1992

Regulation 5

This regulation states quite categorically:

> Every employer shall ensure that his employees are provided with such health surveillance as is appropriate having regard to the risks to their health and safety which are identified by the (risk) assessment.

Health surveillance is a very broad field and must be viewed as part of a general occupational health strategy aimed at protecting the health of people at work. Much will depend on the risks to which people are exposed. What is important is that the form of health surveillance undertaken should be appropriate to the risks.

Health surveillance concentrates on two main groups of employees:

- those at risk of developing further ill health or disability by virtue of their present state of health, such as people exposed to excessive noise levels
- those actually or potentially at risk by virtue of the type of work

they undertake during their employment, for example, radiation workers.

Health surveillance should be carried out by suitably qualified people, such as a doctor with, preferably, a specialist qualification in occupational medicine (occupational physician) and/or an occupational health nurse. It may involve the assessment of hazardous substances or their by-products in the body (by the examination of urine or blood) or of body functions (such as blood pressure, lung function). In some cases, clinical examinations or tests may be necessary. Where medical examinations and inspections are called for, employers must provide suitable facilities on site.

INFORMATION, INSTRUCTION AND TRAINING

Risk assessment is not solely concerned with the identification, measurement and evaluation of risks and the subsequent preventative and protective measures necessary. Inevitably a risk assessment will identify the need for the provision of information, instruction and training for various groups, such as employers, supervisors, contractors.

Regulation 8 of the MHSWR deals with the question of information for employees thus:

> Every employer shall provide his employees with *comprehensible* and *relevant* information on:
>
> (a) the risks to their health and safety identified by the assessment;
>
> (b) the preventative and protective measures;
>
> (c) the procedures referred to in regulation 7(1)(a) (procedures for serious and imminent danger and for danger areas);
>
> (d) the identity of the persons nominated by him in accordance with regulation 7(1)(b) (competent persons to implement emergency procedures); and
>
> (e) the risks notified to him in accordance with regulation 9(1)(c) (shared workplaces).

The ACOP to the regulations clarifies the situation relating to information for employees:

The risk assessment will help identify information which has to be provided to employees under specific regulations, as well as any further information relevant to risks to employees' health and safety. Relevant information on risks and on preventative and protective measures will be limited to what employees need to know to ensure their health and safety. The regulation also requires information to be provided on the emergency arrangements established under regulation 7, including the identity of staff nominated to assist in the event of evacuation. To be *comprehensible*, information must be capable of being understood by the employees to whom it is addressed. This should take account of their level of training, knowledge and experience. Special consideration should be given to any employees with language difficulties or with disabilities which may impede their receipt of information. For employees with little or no understanding of English or who cannot read English, employers any need to make special arrangements. These could include providing translation, using interpreters, or in some cases replacing written notices with clearly understood symbols or diagrams.

Information can be provided in whatever form is most suitable in the circumstances, so long as it is comprehensible.

Instruction and training can take the form of on-the-job one-to-one instruction by a supervisor with individual employees or more formal training sessions. The various stages of training should be recognised, namely induction training, refresher training, skills training, etc., in identifying training needs from a risk assessment.

CONTRACTORS' ACTIVITIES

Where contractors are employed, the risk assessment under regulation 3 of the MHSWR should identify risks to these groups. Contracting activities can include the carrying out of works of construction, repair and maintenance and the provision of various forms of service, such as pest control, window cleaning, catering. These people may be unfamiliar with the risks present on site and the precautions necessary.

OUT-BASED EMPLOYEES

Many employees work on other people's premises, for instance, plant servicing engineers, contract caterers and people who read electricity meters. The risks to which these people are exposed must be considered in the risk assessment process carried out by the employer.

THE IMPORTANCE OF DOCUMENTATION AND ITS INTERNAL ENFORCEMENT

Documentation of risk assessments in particular and other procedures and systems is a legal requirement or, in some cases, an implied legal requirement. From a legal protection viewpoint, employers who have well-documented risk assessments and systems of work are generally viewed more favourably by enforcement officers and the courts than are those who have not. However, mere documentation is not enough – there also needs to be clear evidence of implementation throughout the organisation and at all levels. Managers at all levels must be trained in the interpretation of risk assessment documentation and the organisational procedures and systems for measuring and ensuring compliance.

Further, risk assessments must be linked with in-house codes of practice on issues such as safe systems of work, permit to work systems, cleaning procedures, environmental control and machinery safety.

The risk assessment process

Risk assessment involves:

- the identification of hazards at work
- the weighing up of the risks from the hazards
- deciding how to control the risks
- implementing a control strategy.

A risk assessment has three purposes:

- to identify all the factors that may cause harm to employees and others (*the hazards*)
- to consider what the chances are of that harm actually befalling anyone in the circumstances of a particular case and the possible consequences that could come from it (*the risks*)
- to enable employers to plan, introduce and monitor preventative measures to ensure that the risks are adequately controlled at all times.

Without effective assessment, there can seldom be effective control.

'RISK', 'HAZARD' AND 'DANGER' – THE DISTINCTIONS

In any consideration of the risk assessment process, it is important to distinguish between the terms 'risk', 'hazard' and 'danger'.

'Risk'

'Risk' can be defined in many ways:

- a chance of bad consequences
- exposure to the chance of there being injury or loss
- the probability of harm, damage or injury
- the probability of a hazard leading to personal injury and the severity of that injury
- 'The likelihood that a specified undesired event will occur due to the realisation of a hazard by, or during, work activities or by the products and services created by work activities' (HSE, *Successful Health and Safety Management*)
- the risk from a substance is the likelihood that it will harm a person in the actual circumstances of use, which will depend on:
  - the hazard presented by the substance
  - how it is used
  - how it is controlled
  - who is exposed, to how much and for how long
  - what they are doing, and so on.

Poor control can create a substantial risk even from a substance that presents a low hazard. However, with proper precautions, the risk of being harmed by even the most hazardous substances can be adequately controlled.

'Hazard'

A hazard has been defined thus:

- the result of a departure from the normal situation which has the potential to cause death, injury, damage or loss
- 'The potential to cause harm, including ill health and injury, damage to property, plant, products or the environment, production losses or increased liabilities' (HSE, *Successful Health and Safety Management*).

The hazard presented by a substance is its potential to cause harm.

'Danger'

Danger implies liability or exposure to harm.

HAZARD IDENTIFICATION AND ANALYSIS

Hazards can be identified in many ways. For instance, one of the main objectives of safety monitoring operations, such as a safety audit or a safety inspection, is the identification of hazards. Hazards may further be identified as a result of the investigation of accidents or cases of occupational ill health. A study of current legal requirements applying to a workplace or work activity may also identify hazards that had not previously been considered. Many organisations operate formal hazard reporting procedures whereby employees and others, having identified a workplace hazard, can notify management accordingly. Under the Safety Representatives and Safety Committees Regulations 1977, one of the functions of a trade union-appointed safety representative is that of identifying hazards and reporting these to the employer. Safety management techniques, such as job safety analysis and hazard and operability studies, together with discussions between employers and employees, will also identify hazards. In many cases, hazards are identified by independent personnel, such as insurance company claims investigators, liability surveyors and consultants or by enforcement officers from the HSE, fire authority or local authority.

The various hazard identification techniques are outlined below.

SAFETY MONITORING

Audits and inspections of the workplace are directed at identifying hazards and the action necessary to eliminate or control them. Many people undertake safety monitoring operations, such as health and safety practitioners, enforcement officers, safety representatives, claims investigators and engineering surveyors.

Checklist techniques

A form of checklist can be used to check compliance with good design and operating practices. Such techniques have a number of drawbacks, the main one being the fact that a checklist is only as good as the level of knowledge and experience of the person who produced it!

Consultation

A health and safety committee is an important forum for discussion of hazards identified during safety committee inspections of the workplace or as a result of notification of hazards to members by employees. Other forms of employer/employee discussions, for instance between supervisors and employees, or between engineering management and contractors, in many cases, will identify hazards.

Job safety analysis (JSA)

Job safety analysis (JSA) is an important technique in the design of safe systems of work. It is a technique that identifies all the accident prevention measures appropriate to a particular job or area of work activity, and the behavioural factors that most significantly influence whether or not these measures are implemented. The approach is both diagnostic and descriptive.

JSA can be job-based – say, for machinery operators, fork-lift truck drivers – or activity-based – as in the case of manual handling operations, work at heights or entry into confined spaces. It generally takes place in two specific stages, namely initial JSA and total JSA.

Initial JSA considers the purpose of the job, machinery, equipment and materials used, current protection arrangements, intrinsic hazards, the degree of risk, the work organisation and specific tasks undertaken.

Total JSA then goes on to review the operations involved, the hazards, the skills required, in terms of knowledge and behaviour, the external influences on behaviour, in terms of the nature of the influence (such as noise), the source of the influence (such as machinery) and the activities involved (such as loading procedures) and, finally, the learning method necessary to ensure full understanding of the requirements of the safe system of work by the operators concerned.

Damage control

Damage control and costing techniques emphasise the fact that non-injury accidents are as important as those causing injury. The elimination of non-injury accidents will, in many cases, remove the potential for other forms of accident.

For example, a pallet stack collapses and a falling pallet just misses an operator standing close by. No injury results and, therefore, no accident is recorded, but there may be damage to products, pallets, the building fabric, plant and fittings. However, the next time a pallet stack collapses, someone could be seriously injured or killed. This accident is recorded.

In these two situations, the correction of the cause of the first collapse (bad stacking, use of defective pallets, stacking too high or stacking on an uneven floor) would have prevented the injury following the second pallet stack collapse. Moreover, the independent assessment of costs incurred as a result of damage accidents, such as repairs to plant and equipment, replacement items, maintenance costs, structural repairs, labour costs, etc. will emphasise the need for safe systems of work and higher levels of supervision.

Damage control techniques aim to provide a safe place of work and call for the keenest observation and cooperation on the part of all staff who see or experience a condition that may lead to an accident, such as a damaged guard or safety mechanism on a machine. Damage control relies heavily on the operation of a hazard reporting scheme, covering damage and defects in plant, machinery, structural items, vehicles, etc. An example of a hazard report form in shown in Figure 3.1 (overleaf).

Project safety analysis (PSA)

While existing risks may be identified and assessed following various

HAZARD REPORT

No. 000001

1 **Report** (to be completed by person identifying hazard)

*Date*__________ *Time*__________ *Department* ____________________

Reported to: (Verbal)__________ (Written) ____________________

Description of hazard ____

____

*Signature*____________________ *Position* ____________________

2 **Action** (to be completed by Departmental Manager/Supervisor)

Hazard verified YES/NO *Date*__________ *Time*__________

Remedial action (including changes in system of work)

____

____

*Action to be taken by: Name*________________ *Signature* ____________

**Priority rating 1 2 3 4 5* __________*Estimated cost £* ________________

Interim precautions ____

____

____

*Signature*____________________ *Date* ____________________

3 **Financial approval** (to be completed by unit manager or his assistant)

The expenditure to eliminate the above hazard is approved.

*Signature*____________________ *(Manager/Assistant Manager) Date*______

4 **Completion** (the remedial action described above is complete)

Signature (Departmental Manager) ____________________ *Date*______

*Actual cost £*______

5 **Safety Officer's check**

I have checked completion of the above work and confirm that the hazard has been eliminated.

*Signature*____________________ (Safety Officer) *Date/time*____________

***Priority ratings:**
1 (immediate)
2 (48 hours)
3 (7 days)
4 (1 month)
5 (3 months)

● **FIG 3.1 Example of a hazard reporting form**

forms of safety monitoring, PSA, undertaken as a joint exercise by an engineering manager, architect, plant and equipment supplier and installer, health and safety specialist and other specialists, helps to ensure that account is taken of accumulated experience, knowledge of the technology and best practice in the initial design of projects. PSA should be carried out at the design stage of all projects, both large and small. A typical analysis procedure is shown in Figure 3.2 (overleaf).

Failure mode and effect analysis (FMEA)

This technique is based on identifying the possible failure modes of each component of a system and predicting the consequences of that failure. For instance, if a control valve fails, it could result in too much flow in the system, too much pressure or the production of an undesired chemical reaction. As a result, attention is paid to these consequences at the design stage of a project and in the preparation of planned preventative maintenance systems.

Fault tree analysis (FTA)

The process of FTA begins with consideration of a chosen 'top event', such as a major fire or an explosion, and then assesses the combination of failures and conditions that could cause that event. It is widely used in quantitative risk analysis, particularly where control over process controls is critical if safety standards are to be met.

Event tree analysis (ETA)

Similar in many respects to FTA, ETA works from a selected 'initiating event', such as a pressure control failure. Essentially, it is a systematic representation of all the possible states of the processing system conditional to the specific initiating event and relevant for a certain type of outcome, such as a pollution incident or a major fire.

PROJECT SAFETY ANALYSIS

Project title ________________________________ *Date of analysis* ____________

Dangerous substances

1 List all substances that are:
- flammable
- explosive
- corrosive
- toxic (state effects)
- have other specific hazards (state hazards).

2 State whether each substance is a:
- raw material
- intermediate product
- final product or by-product
- waste material.

3 List the points where such substances are encountered in the process by process description, equipment and cross-references to the operating process manual.

4 List significant physical properties, including:
- incompatibility with other chemicals
- chemical reaction rates
- conditions of instability
- other pertinent properties.

5 Show your sources of data and list the available information sources on critical points.

Process hazards

1 List the maximum operating pressures under both normal and abnormal operating conditions.
2 State the form of pressure relief provided.
State the location of pressure relief provided.
State the condition of the relief devices.
3 State the date when the relief devices were last tested.
State whether personnel are exposed to risk or injury on discharge of emergency relief devices.
4 List the maximum permissible operating temperatures and sources of heat.
Identify the over-temperature controls that are provided for abnormal operating conditions.
State the protection provided to hot surfaces to protect personnel from burns.

• **FIG 3.2 Project safety analysis**

5 State the dangers that may be present if process reaction conditions are deviated from in the following ways and the protection procedures necessary should these occur:

- abnormal temperature
- abnormal reaction times
- instrument failure
- adding materials at the wrong stage
- the materials added
- material flow stoppage
- equipment leaks, both out of the process and into the process
- agitation failure
- loss of inert gas blanket
- error in value or switch operations
- blocked relief line
- failure of relief line
- material spillage on floor or dispersal to air.

Waste disposal

1 List the gaseous stack effluents and concentrations, together with smoke characteristics.
State whether scrubbers, electrostatic or centrifugal removal of stack effluents is needed.
2 State the approved height of the stacks.
3 State the direction of prevailing winds as they relate to exposed areas.
4 State the effluents that are run through waste disposal, from any point in the process, and the method of transfer.
State their pH, relative toxicity, flammability and miscibility with water.
5 State whether or not waste chemicals can react with other waste chemicals in waste disposal systems and create hazards/difficulties.
6 State the procedure required to prevent flammable liquids from reaching sewers.
7 List any special hazardous solid waste products, such as asbestos, and the procedure for handling these.

Ventilation

1 State the frequency of air changes required.
State the frequency of checking ventilation equipment on a regular basis and the responsibility for this.
2 State whether or not exhaust ventilation is required for specific processes.
List the air flow rates to be achieved and the responsibility for checking this.
3 State what the risk is of the ventilation intakes recirculating contaminants.

Piping systems

1 Confirm that piping systems are adequately supported with permanent hangers.
2 Confirm that pipework is of the proper material and scheduled thickness for its use.

3 Confirm that pressure tests for critical services and processes are scheduled and on a regular basis.
4 Confirm that any bumping and/or tripping hazards are protected.
5 Confirm that safe access is provided to all valves.

Electrical equipment

1 Confirm that all hazardous locations are classified.
2 Confirm that all electrical equipment complies with the above including:

- lighting
- wiring and switches
- motors
- instrumentation
- intercoms, telephones, clocks, etc.

3 Confirm that all earthing meets the required standard.
4 Identify the person responsible for checking the above and frequency of checking.

Access

1 Confirm that two routes of access are provided to all occupied parts of buildings.

Working platforms

1 Confirm that safety rails with toe boards are provided on all platforms over 1 metre high and all occupied enclosed portions of roof.
2 Confirm that safe means of access are provided to all working platforms.

Fire protection

1 Confirm that all fire doors are checked on a regular basis.
2 Confirm that exposed steel supporting major items of equipment is fire-proofed.
3 Confirm whether or not an automatic or manually operated sprinkler protection system is installed.
4 Confirm whether or not special fire extinguishing equipment is provided.
5 State the number, type and location of fire appliances and the system for ensuring regular servicing of such appliances.
6 Identify the location of fire hydrants and hose reels.
7 Identify the locations of fire alarm boxes and building evacuation alarms.
8 State whether or not any flammable substances are handled in the open.
9 Specify the amount stored and the location of flammable substances in operating buildings.
10 Specify the amount stored, location and the system for protection of flammable liquids and gases stored outdoors.

Personnel, equipment and facilities

1 Specify the type of protection overclothing provided.

FIG 3.2 (Continued)

2 Confirm that safety boots/shoes are provided and worn.
3 Confirm that gloves/gauntlets are provided and worn for certain jobs.
4 Confirm that the correct type of eye protection is provided and used where there is a risk of eye injury.
5 Confirm that safety helmets/bump caps are provided and worn by all operators.
6 Confirm that respirator stations are adequately identified and maintained.
7 State the frequency of changing of overalls particularly where there is a risk of heavy soiling.
8 Confirm that an amenity block of WCs, urinals, wash basins, showers, hot and cold water, and a separate mess room, is provided.
9 Confirm that a first aid facility is provided, together with trained first aiders.

Training

1 Confirm that operating manuals are available and have been provided.
2 Confirm that health and safety components of routine training for operators have been identified.
3 Confirm that there is a training schedule and that staff are adequately trained.
4 Confirm that the effectiveness of training is monitored.
5 Confirm that occupational health practices are adequately covered in training.
6 Confirm that safety rules have been written, published and are enforced.

Legal requirements

1 Confirm compliance with the Health and Safety at Work, etc. Act 1974 with particular reference to:

- provision and maintenance of plant and systems of work that are safe and without risks to health
- arrangements for the safe use, handling, storage and transport of articles and substances
- provision of information, instruction, training and supervision of employees
- provision of a safe place of work, with safe means of access to and egress from it
- provision and maintenance of a safe working environment
- provisions for consultation on health and safety issues
- preparation and presentation of a statement of health and safety policy.

2 Confirm compliance with the current regulations, in particular:

- Construction (General Provisions) Regulations 1961
- Construction (Lifting Operations) Regulations 1961
- Construction (Health and Welfare) Regulations 1966
- Construction (Working Places) Regulations 1966
- Construction (Head Protection) Regulations 1989
- Construction (Design and Management) Regulations 1994

- Highly Flammable Liquids and Liquefied Petroleum Gases Regulations 1972
- Safety Signs Regulations 1980
- Health and Safety (First Aid) Regulations 1981
- Building Regulations 1985
- Ionising Radiations Regulations 1985
- Reporting of Injuries, Diseases and Dangerous Occurrences Regulations 1995
- Noise at Work Regulations 1989
- Electricity at Work Regulations 1989
- Pressure Systems and Transportable Gas Containers Regulations 1989
- Health and Safety (Information for Employees) Regulations 1989
- Management of Health and Safety at Work Regulations 1992
- Workplace (Health, Safety and Welfare) Regulations 1992
- Provision and Use of Work Equipment Regulations 1992
- Personal Protective Equipment at Work Regulations 1992
- Manual Handling Operations Regulations 1992
- Health and Safety (Display Screen Equipment) Regulations 1992
- Control of Substances Hazardous to Health Regulations 1994.

3 Confirm that risk assessments have been prepared and are available under:

- Noise at Work Regulations 1989
- Management of Health and Safety at Work Regulations 1992
- Provision and Use of Work Equipment Regulations 1992
- Personal Protective Equipment Regulations 1992
- Manual Handling Operations Regulations 1992
- Health and Safety (Display Screen Equipment) Regulations 1992
- Control of Substances Hazardous to Health Regulations 1994.

4 Confirm that competent persons have been appointed in compliance with:

- Management of Health and Safety at Work Regulations 1992
- Construction (General Provisions) Regulations 1961
- Construction (Lifting Operations) Regulations 1961
- Construction (Working Places) Regulations 1966
- Construction (Design and Management) Regulations 1994
- Pressure Systems and Transportable Gas Containers Regulations 1989
- Electricity at Work Regulations 1989.

Consequence analysis

This is a feature of risk analysis that considers the physical effects of a particular process failure and the damage caused by these effects. It is carried out to form a viewpoint on potentially serious hazardous outcomes of accidents and their possible consequences for people and the environment. Consequence analysis should act as a tool in the decision-making process in a safety study that incorporates the following features:

- description of the process system to be investigated
- identification of the undesirable events
- determination of the magnitude of the resulting physical effects
- determination of the damage
- estimation of the probability of the occurrence of calculated damage
- assessment of risk against calculated criteria.

The outcome of consequence analysis is fourfold. It is:

- for the chemical and process industries, to obtain information about all known and unknown effects that are of importance when something goes wrong in the plant and how to deal with possible catastrophic events
- for the designing industries, to obtain information on how to minimise the consequences of accidents
- for the workers in the processing plant and people living in the immediate vicinity, to give them an understanding of their personal situation and the measures being taken to protect them
- for the enforcement authorities to consider the adequacy of current legislative controls and the need for revision of the same.

The logical chain of consequence analysis is shown in Figure 3.3 (overleaf). The first link in the chain is a description of the technical system to be investigated. In order to identify the undesirable events, it is necessary to construct a scenario of possible incidents. The next stage is to undertake model calculations in which damage-level criteria are taken into account. Following discussions by the assessment team, conclusions can be drawn as to the possible consequences.

Feedback from the model calculations to the scenario is included, as the linking of the *outputs* from the scenario to the *inputs* of the models may cause difficulties. There is also feedback from the damage criteria to the model calculations, in case these criteria should be influenced by possible threshold values of the enforcement authorities.

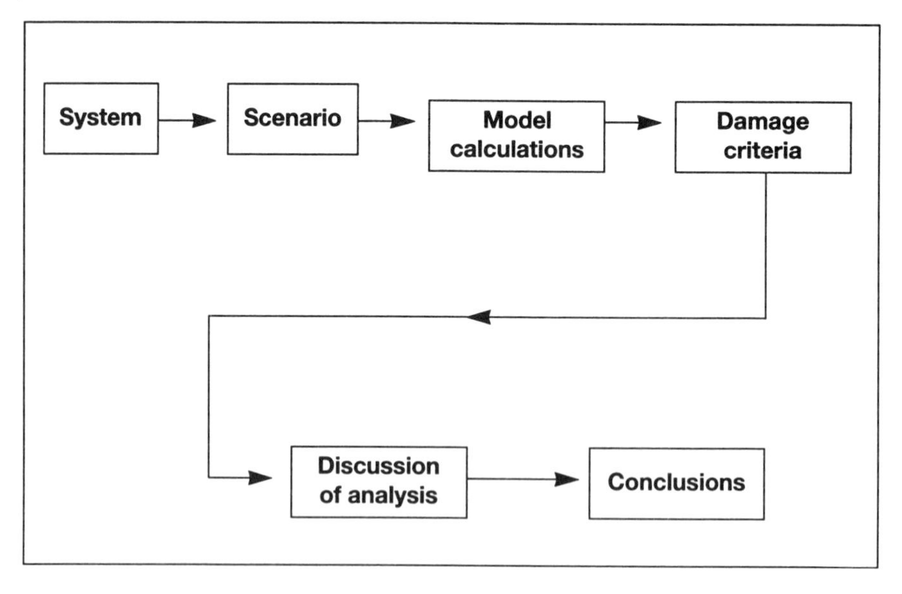

• **FIG 3.3 Logical chain of consequence analysis**

Hazard indices

There are two empirical methods for identifying hazards, namely the Dow and Mond indices, which systematically identify and provide a method for ranking hazards.

The *Dow Fire and Explosion Index* primarily aims to identify fire, explosion and chemical reactivity hazards during a plant design, and is used for audit purposes on existing plant. This index is derived from:

- material factor hazards
- general process hazards
- special process hazards.

A *material factor* is an indication of the energy potential of the most hazardous materials. It depends on two properties, namely flammability and reactivity, which are listed in the Dow guide. A *hazard factor* is calculated for each process 'unit' and then modified by two further weighting factors – *general process hazards* and *special process hazards.* Special process hazards include process temperatures, pressure levels, sizes of inventory of flammable materials, potential for corrosion erosion, and proximity of the process to flammable range. The design and protective features of the process are assessed in order to determine their adequacy.

The *Mond Index* was developed following the Flixborough disaster. It expands on the Dow index as it includes wider consideration of continuous and batch processes in the storage and loading/unloading areas and these are not considered fully in the Dow index. The evaluation of hazards from materials, reactions and toxicity is also more extensive in the Mond index than in the Dow index.

With this system, an installation is divided into 'units'. A *material factor* is calculated for each unit based on the heat of combustion. Each material factor is weighted or modified according to:

- the properties of materials in the process
- the quantities involved
- the type of process and how difficult it is to control
- the process conditions
- acute health hazards (toxicity)
- process layout.

The *layout factor* is intended to bring out more clearly the advantageous effects that spacing, access, structure, heights, drainage, etc. can have on hazard potential.

When these weighting factors are combined with the material factors, a numerical value for a fire and explosion index is arrived at. This was subsequently replaced by categories, which allow the overall hazard to be ranked by comparison with the value of the index for 'units of known fire and explosion risk'.

Accident data

The use of accident data as an element of the hazard identification and risk assessment process is common. Various forms of accident data are collected by organisations and a number of standard indices are used, such as accident incidence, frequency, severity and duration rates. These rates are based on information generally compiled from accident reports. As such, they have limited application due to the well-established fact that, in some organisations, a substantial number of accidents are never reported, either internally or to the enforcement authorities. Accident data do, however, indicate trends in accident experience and provide feedback for incorporation in future risk assessment and accident prevention strategies.

The following rates are used:

$$\text{Frequency rate} = \frac{\text{Total number of accidents}}{\text{Total number of man hours worked}} \times 1{,}000{,}000$$

$$\text{Incidence rate} = \frac{\text{Total number of accidents}}{\text{Average number of people exposed}} \times 1{,}000$$

$$\text{Severity rate} = \frac{\text{Total number of days lost}}{\text{Total man hours worked}}$$

$$\text{Mean duration rate} = \frac{\text{Total number of days lost}}{\text{Total number of accidents}}$$

$$\text{Duration rate} = \frac{\text{Number of man hours worked}}{\text{Total number of accidents}}$$

A study by H. Amis and R. T. Booth in 1991 (*Monitoring Health and Safety Management*, Institute of Occupational Safety and Health, 1991) questioned the significance of accident statistics as a measure of health and safety performance. Its conclusions regarding accident statistics were as follows.

- They measure failure, not success.
- They are difficult to use in staff appraisal.
- They are subject to random fluctuations; there should not be enough accidents to carry out statistical evaluation. Is safety fully controlled if, by chance, there are no accidents over a period?
- They reflect the success or otherwise of safety measures taken some time ago. There is a time delay in judging the effectiveness of new measures.
- They do not measure the incidence of occupational diseases where there is a prolonged latent period.

- They measure injury severity, not necessarily the potential seriousness of the accident. Strictly, they do not even do this. Time off work as a result of an injury may not correlate well with true injury severity. Data may be affected by the known variations in the propensity of people to take time off work for sickness in different parts of the country.
- They may under-report (or over-report) injuries and may vary as a result of subtle differences in reporting criteria.
- They are particularly limited for assessing the future risk of high-consequence, low-probability accidents (a fatal accident rate based on data from single fatalities may not be a good predictor of the risk of multiple fatal emergencies.)

The crucial point is that counting numbers of accidents provides incomplete, untimely and possibly misleading answers to the questions:

- are we implementing our safety plan fully?
- is it the right plan?

Where management has not drawn up a safety plan, however, counting accidents is the only measure of safety performance available – apart, of course, from auditing compliance with statutory hardware requirements. This is why safety management via accident rate comparison is attractive to the less competent and committed employer.

Hazard and operability studies (HAZOPS)

HAZOPS is defined as the application of a formal critical examination to the process and engineering intentions of new facilities to assess the hazard potential from misuse or malfunction of individual items of equipment and the consequential effects on the facility as a whole.

The aim of HAZOPS is to assess the hazard potential arising from the incorrect operation of individual items of plant and equipment and the consequential effects on the whole system. It is a structured technique that was developed for use predominantly in projects involving large chemical manufacturing installations where individual plant failures could result in the catastrophic failure of the main installation. Once the hazard potential has been assessed, remedial action is then usually possible at a very early stage of the project with maximum effectiveness and minimal costs.

These studies examine the potential for error among operators, with particular regard to new plant and machinery, on the basis that the perpetuation of errors in design can result in accidents, plant stoppage and loss of production. While unsuspected hazards may be revealed by HAZOPS, the use of a formal checklist in engineering design departments helps to ensure that account is taken of accumulated experience, knowledge of the technology and best practice in initial design.

THE CLASSIFICATION OF HAZARDOUS AGENTS

Hazardous agents can be classified on the basis of physical, chemical, biological and natural phenomena.

Physical agencies

Examples of physical agencies include:

- gravity (falls of people, materials and objects)
- manual handling operations
- the use of hand tools
- the moving parts of machinery and plant and/or their loads
- various types of vehicle, whether free-moving or on tracks
- electricity (shock, fire and explosion)
- pressure, including explosive pressure rises
- radiation
- noise and vibration.

Chemical agencies

Examples of chemical agencies include:

- fire
- explosions
- contamination, whether direct or indirect, from any harmful chemical source.

Biological agencies

Examples of biological agencies are:

- animals, including human sources
- micro-organisms (bacteria, viruses, etc.)
- plants and various forms of vegetation.

Natural phenomena

Examples of natural phenomena include:

- extremes of heat and cold
- water
- weather conditions, such as wind, lightning, fog and driving rain.

Natural hazards not only cause harm in their own right, but also exacerbate other hazards, such as the operation of vehicles in fog or snow.

HAZARD ANALYSIS AND RISK ASSESSMENT

For several industries, the level of risk can be judged from relevant accident statistics. In other cases, this is not realistic. Some form of risk assessment, of both a qualitative and quantitative nature, is essential. These techniques are most effectively applied during the planning, process design and design engineering stages of projects when it is possible to make changes at least cost.

The effectiveness of hazard analysis and risk assessment involves a number of practical considerations. Before commencing a study, the objectives, scope, purpose and fundamental assumptions must be clearly defined and stated, together with system boundaries, as well as the information regarding intended design, operation and layout.

The identification of hazards is a technical procedure that should follow an established pattern. It must be assumed that sound engineering standards, operating and maintenance procedures and safety policies are already being employed. It is essential to distinguish between continuing hazards (namely those hazards inherent in the process) and those hazards that can arise as a direct result of equipment process failure, such as fire and toxic releases.

Several qualitative approaches to hazard identification that provide a more formalised and structured procedure can be used. These procedures may vary, from the use of checklists to HAZOPS.

Risk assessment procedure

The following steps are involved:

- the hazards can be identified and ranked according to their possible effects using FMEA
- the consequences can be analysed using ETA
- the risks are assessed quantitatively by allocating numerical values based on the frequency of the hazards arising or the probability (likelihood) of their occurrence
- risks can be quantified further by means of *reliability technology,* which assesses the probability of equipment and/or process failures, and FTA, which quantifies the frequency or probability of an undesired event, such as a boiler explosion.

Evaluation of risk

This stage of the risk assessment determines whether the level of risk is acceptable or unacceptably high and warrants some form of corrective action. There are no standard criteria for the acceptability or otherwise of risk.

Corrective measures

Where the level of risk is unacceptable, corrective measures are required to either reduce the probability of the hazard occurring and/or mitigate the consequences. Corrective measures include design changes, effective protection systems, procedural or organisational changes. Corrective measures should ensure that all existing hazards are eliminated or controlled and no new hazards are introduced in the process.

RISK ASSESSMENT – KEY POINTS

The ACOP to the MHSWR makes the following points. A suitable and sufficient risk assessment should:

- identify the significant risks arising out of work.

This means focusing on those risks that are liable to arise because of the work activity.

Trivial risks can usually be ignored, as can risks arising from routine activities associated with life in general – unless the work activity compounds those risks, or there is evidence of significant relevance to the particular work activity.

Employers and the self-employed are expected to take reasonable steps (such as reading HSE Guidance Notes, the trade press, company or supplier manuals, etc.) to familiarise themselves with the hazards and risks in their work.

A suitable and sufficient risk assessment should also:

- enable the employer to identify and prioritise the measures that need to be taken to comply with the relevant statutory provisions
- be appropriate to the nature of the work and remain valid for a reasonable period of time.

This will enable the risk assessment and the significant findings to be used positively by management, say, to change working procedures or introduce medium- to long-term controls.

For relatively static operations, the risk assessment must be such that it is not necessary to repeat it every time someone is exposed to a hazard in comparable circumstances.

For more dynamic activities – where the detailed work activity may change fairly frequently or the workplace itself changes and develops (such as on a temporary work site or where the work involves peripatetic workers moving from site to site – the risk assessment might have to concentrate more on the broad range of risks that might arise so that detailed planning and employee training can take account of those risks and enable them to be controlled as and when they arise.

Risk assessment in practice (HSC)

See pages 6 to 9.

The HSE further advises that:

- assessments must be *adequate* – they must be sufficient to guide employers' judgements about the measures they should take to fulfil their legal obligations
- assessments must cover all the risks to the health and safety of *employees* that they are exposed to at work
- assessments must cover risks to *non-employees* who may be affected by the employer's activities/operations, such as members of the public or contractors operating in the workplace
- whenever new or changed risks are encountered, the employer must *revise* his original assessment, so a regular review is advised as part of good management practice
- where employers employ five or more employees, the assessment must be *in writing*
- where groups of employees are especially at risk, the *groups* must be identified as part of the assessments, for example, young, inexperienced or handicapped workers
- in complicated high-risk industries where quantified risk assessment may be appropriate, the professional expertise of outside consultants may be required.

Management action plan for risk assessment (HSE)

Such a plan should include the following points:

- appoint a responsible person, or small representative group, to compile a list of harmful agencies (hazards) present on the premises or involved with the organisation's operations and activities

- circulate the preliminary list of hazards to all interested parties for their comments and any additions, say to directors, managers, supervisors and safety representatives
- submit the amended list to the hazard assessment group for scrutiny to establish a *probable frequency rating* and, in order to do this a scale, such as the following typical one, should be used:

  1 = a highly improbable occurrence
  2 = a remotely possible but known occurrence
  3 = an occasional occurrence
  4 = a fairly frequent occurrence
  5 = a frequent and regular occurrence
  6 = almost a certainty
- establish a *potential severity rating* for the identified hazards, using the following scale:

  1 = negligible injuries
  2 = minor injuries
  3 = major injuries
  4 = single fatality
  5 = multiple fatalities
  6 = multiple fatalities (including fatalities off site)
- compile a list of *risk rating numbers* by using the rating table shown in Table 3.1 (overleaf), that is multiply the ratings derived from the two points above – the probable frequency and potential severity ratings (such risk ratings enable the most serious hazards – those with the highest numbers and hence the highest priority – to be considered first)
- match the identified risks with the measures that exist at present for controlling them and ascertain whether or not more needs to be done for the control measures to be as effective as the judged risks merit (help from specialists may be necessary at this stage)
- taking each identified operation on a department by department basis, compile a formal assessment record for each
- documents arising from the assessments should be incorporated within the organisation's statement of health and safety policy, so that they can be seen to be part of the overall safety culture

- to arrive at decisions about ratings (covered in third and fourth points above), the assessment group should examine past records of accidents and incidents, near misses and cases of occupational ill health among employees and former employees.

Table 3.1 Risk rating table (HSE)

		Severity					
		6	5	4	3	2	1
	6	36	30	24	18	12	6
	5	30	25	20	15	10	5
Probable frequency	4	24	20	16	12	8	4
	3	18	15	12	9	6	3
	2	12	10	8	6	4	2
	1	6	5	4	3	2	1

Risk rating

Recording the risk assessment

The significant findings of the risk assessment must be recorded. The significant findings should include:

- the *significant hazards* identified in the risk assessment – that is, those hazards that might pose serious risk to workers or others who might be affected by the work activity if they were not properly controlled

- the *existing control measures* in place and the extent to which they control the risks (this need not replicate details of measures more fully described in works manuals and so on but could refer to them)
- the *population* that may be affected by these significant risks or hazards, including any *groups* of employees who are especially at risk.

OTHER APPROACHES TO RISK ASSESSMENT

It should be recognised that risk assessment is not a precise science and there are no specific rules or requirements as to the quantification of risk or the actual format for a risk assessment. On the other hand, a risk assessment should satisfy both the general requirements of the MHSWR and the more specific requirements of other regulations, such as the Manual Handling Operations Regulations 1992.

The assessment of risk fundamentally considers a number of factors, namely:

- the likelihood or probability that an accident or incident could occur
- the severity of the outcome, in terms of injury, damage or loss
- the number of people affected
- the frequency of exposure to risk
- the maximum possible loss.

All these factors can be quantified using numerical scales, as seen earlier in this chapter. Let us look at some more such scales.

Probability, severity and frequency

A simple quantitative method of assessing risk is to use risk ratings, taking into account the factors of probability, severity and frequency on a scale from 1 to 10 in each case (some systems use only probability and severity factors).

risk rating = probability (P) x severity (S) x frequency (F)

which gives a rating between 1 and 1000. Standard probability, severity and frequency indices are used (see Tables 3.2, 3.3 and 3.4 overleaf).

Table 3.2 Probability scale

Probability index	*Description*
10	Inevitable
9	Almost certain
8	Very likely
7	Probable
6	More than even chance
5	Even chance
4	Less than even chance
3	Improbable
2	Very improbable
1	Almost impossible

Table 3.3 Severity scale

Severity index	*Description*
10	Death
9	Permanent total incapacity
8	Permanent severe incapacity
7	Permanent slight incapacity
6	Absent from work for more than three weeks with subsequent recurring incapacity
5	Absent from work for more than three weeks but with subsequent complete recovery
4	Absent from work for more than three days but less than three weeks with subsequent complete recovery
3	Absent from work for less than three days with complete recovery
2	Minor injury with no lost time and complete recovery
1	No human injury expected

Table 3.4 Frequency scale

Frequency index	*Description*
10	Hazard permanently present
9	Hazard arises every 30 seconds
8	Hazard arises every minute
7	Hazard arises every 30 minutes
6	Hazard arises every hour
5	Hazard arises every shift
4	Hazard arises once a week
3	Hazard arises once a month
2	Hazard arises every year
1	Hazard arises every five years

The urgency or priority of action in respect of a particular risk associated with a task or activity can be quantified as shown in Table 3.5.

Table 3.5 Priority of action

Priority index	*Description*
800–1000	Immediate action
600–800	Action within the next seven days
400–600	Action within the next month
200–400	Action within the next year
Below 200	No immediate action necessary, but keep under review.

Frequency, severity, maximum possible loss and probability

A further risk assessment formula involving frequency, severity and maximum possible loss can also be used:

risk rating = frequency x (severity + MPL + probability)

where

severity = number of people at risk
frequency = frequency of the occurrence
maximum possible loss is based on a scale from 1 to 50.

The criteria for assessing risk using the above criteria are shown in Tables 3.6 and 3.7 respectively, together with those for priority of action in Table 3.8.

Table 3.6 Typical scale of maximum possible loss

Maximum possible loss index	*Description*
50	Fatal
45	Loss of two limbs/eyes
40	Loss of hearing
30	Loss of one limb/eye
15	Broken arm
1	Scratch

Table 3.7 Typical probability scale

Probability index	*Description*
50	Imminent
35	Hourly
25	Daily
15	Once a week
10	Once a month
5	Once a year
1	Unlikely

Table 3.8 Priority of action

Risk rating	*Urgency of action*
Over 100	Immediate
50–100	Today
25–50	Within a week
10–25	Within a month
1–10	Within three months

MODEL (GENERIC) RISK ASSESSMENTS

These are assessments produced once only for a given activity or type of workplace.

In cases where organisations have similar workplaces, such as retail depots and workshops, or situations where the same activity is undertaken, such as manual handling or dispensing chemicals from bulk, then a *generic risk assessment* could be carried out to cover these locations and activities (see Chapter 6, Workplace and work activity risk assessments).

Effective generic risk assessments

For generic risk assessments to be effective:

- 'worst case' situations must be considered

- provision should be made on the assessment record to monitor the implementation of the controls that are or are not relevant at a particular location.

Where risks are specific to one situation only, these risks may need to be incorporated in a separate part of the generic risk assessment.

MAINTAINING THE RISK ASSESSMENT

Any risk assessment must be *maintained*. This means that any significant change to a workplace, work process or activity, or the introduction of any new process, activity or operation, should be subject to risk assessment. If new hazards come to light, then these should also be subject to risk assessment. The risk assessment, should, in any case, be periodically reviewed and updated. This is best achieved by a suitable combination of safety inspection and monitoring techniques, which require corrective and/or additional action where the need is identified. Typical monitoring systems include:

- preventative maintenance inspections
- safety representative/committee inspections
- safety tours and inspections
- occupational health surveys
- air monitoring
- safety audits.

Useful information on checking performance against control standards can also be obtained reactively from the following activities:

- accident and ill health investigation
- investigation of damage to plant, equipment and vehicles
- investigation of 'near miss' situations.

The frequency of review depends on the level of risk in the operation. Further, if a serious accident occurs in the organisation – or elsewhere but is possible in the organisation – and where a check on the risk assessment shows no actual assessment or a gap in assessment procedures, then a review is necessary.

HSE SPECIMEN RISK ASSESSMENT

In 1994, the HSE provided specimen risk assessment documentation in their publication *Five Steps to Risk Assessment* (HSE Enquiry Points, 1994). This document is reproduced in Figures 3.4a to d.

Assessment of risk for

Company name ______________________________

Company address ______________________________

______________________________ *Postcode* ______________

Assessment undertaken (date) ______________ *Signed* ______________

Assessment review date ______________________________

Hazard

Look only for hazards you could reasonably expect to result in significant harm under the conditions in your workplace. Use the following examples as a guide:

- slipping/tripping hazards
- electricity
- dust and/or fume
- work at heights
- ejection of material from machines
- pressure systems
- vehicles
- fire
- chemicals
- moving parts of machinery
- manual handling
- noise
- poor lighting
- low temperature.

List hazards here:

● **FIG 3.4a Risk assessment document (HSE)**

Who might be harmed?

There is no need to list individuals by name. Just think about groups of people doing similar work or who may be affected, such as:

- office staff
- maintenance personnel
- contractors
- people sharing your workplace
- operators
- cleaners
- members of the public.

Pay particular attention to:

- staff with disabilities
- visitors
- inexperienced staff
- lone workers.

They may be more vulnerable.

List groups of people who are especially at risk from the significant hazards you have identified.

- **FIG 3.4b Who might be harmed?**

3

Is the risk adequately controlled?

Have you already taken precautions against the risks from the hazards you listed? For example, have you provided:

- adequate information, instruction and training?
- adequate systems of procedures?

Do the precautions:

- meet the standards set by a legal requirement?
- comply with a recognised industry standard?
- represent good practice?
- reduce risk as far as reasonably practicable?

If so, then the risks are adequately controlled, but you need to indicate the precautions you have in place. You may refer to procedures, manuals, company rules, etc. giving this information.

List existing controls here or note where the information may be found:

- **FIG 3.4c Is the risk adequately controlled?**

What further action is necessary to control the risk?

What more could you reasonably do for those risks you found were not adequately controlled?
You will need to give priority to those risks that affect large numbers of people and/or could result in serious harm. Apply the principles below when taking further action, if possible in the following order:

- remove the risk completely
- try a less risky option
- prevent access to the hazards
- organise work to reduce exposure to the hazards
- issue PPE
- provide welfare facilities, eg washing facilities first aid

List the risks that are not adequately controlled and the action you will take where it is reasonably practicable to do more. You are entitled to take cost into account, unless the risk is high.

FIG 3.4d What further action is necessary to control the risk?

CONCLUSION

As stated earlier in this chapter, there are no fixed rules regarding how a risk assessment should be undertaken or, indeed, recorded. On this basis, organisations have got to decide on a system that meets their needs, taking into account legal requirements, the range and scale of their activities and the risks inherent in their business and/or operations. *Five Steps to Risk Assessment* provides a useful starting point for the exercise. The risk assessment process is further summarised in Figure 3.5.

Chapters 4 to 10 (which should be read in conjunction with the legal requirements for risk assessment incorporated in Chapter 1) provide guidance and specimen risk assessment documentation to cover a number of areas where risk assessments are required – for instance, in the case of manual handling operations, the use of substances hazardous to heath and where employees may be exposed to noise. The general principles of risk assessment outlined in this chapter should be applied to these more specific forms of risk assessment.

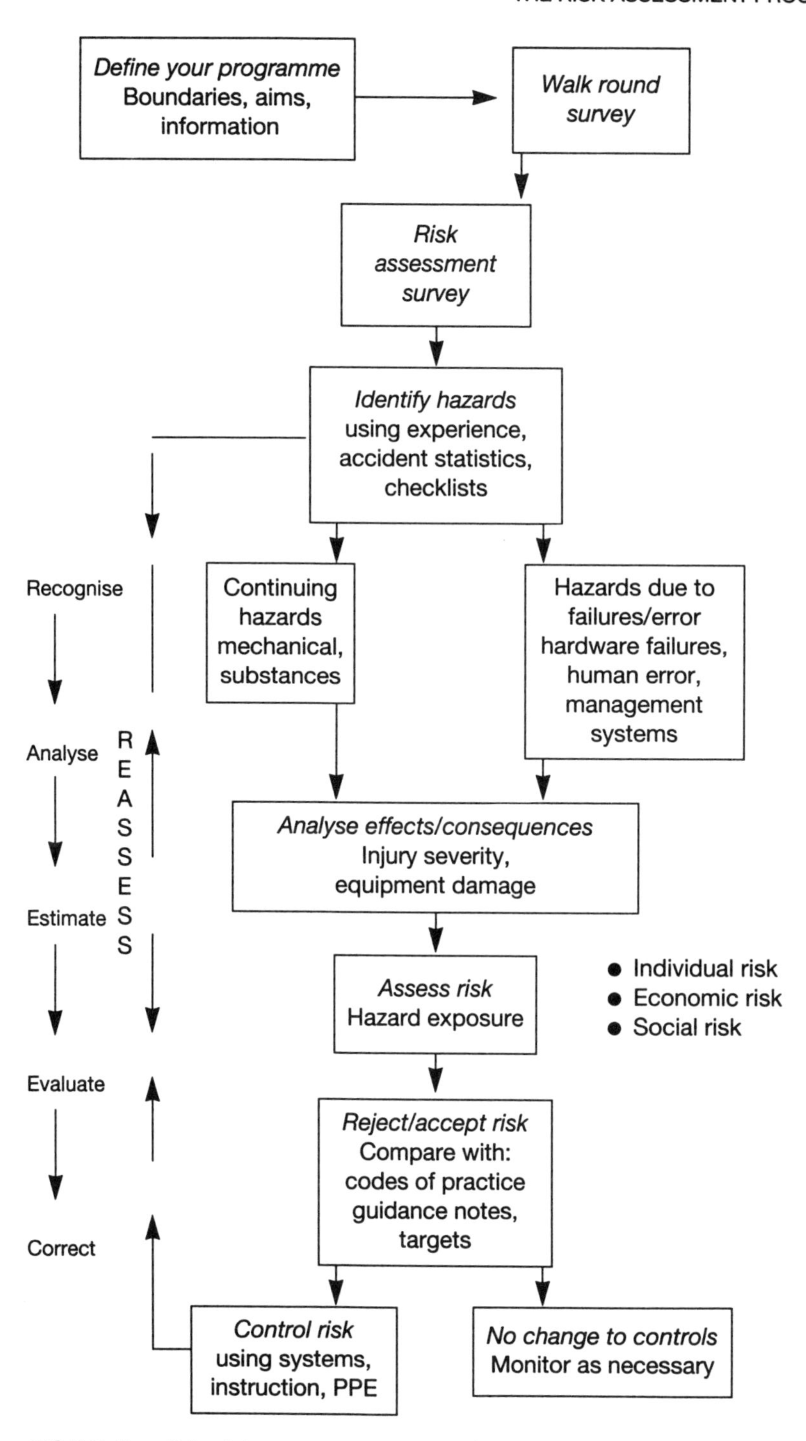

FIG 3.5 Possible risk assessment procedure

Finally, risk assessment must not be viewed in isolation. It is an integral feature of the health and safety management process, which is concerned with the continuing improvement of health and safety performance throughout an organisation. As such, it must be related to the statement of health and safety policy and ancillary documentation, inspection and maintenance systems and the system for auditing performance. The relationship of risk assessment to these management procedures is shown in Figure 3.6.

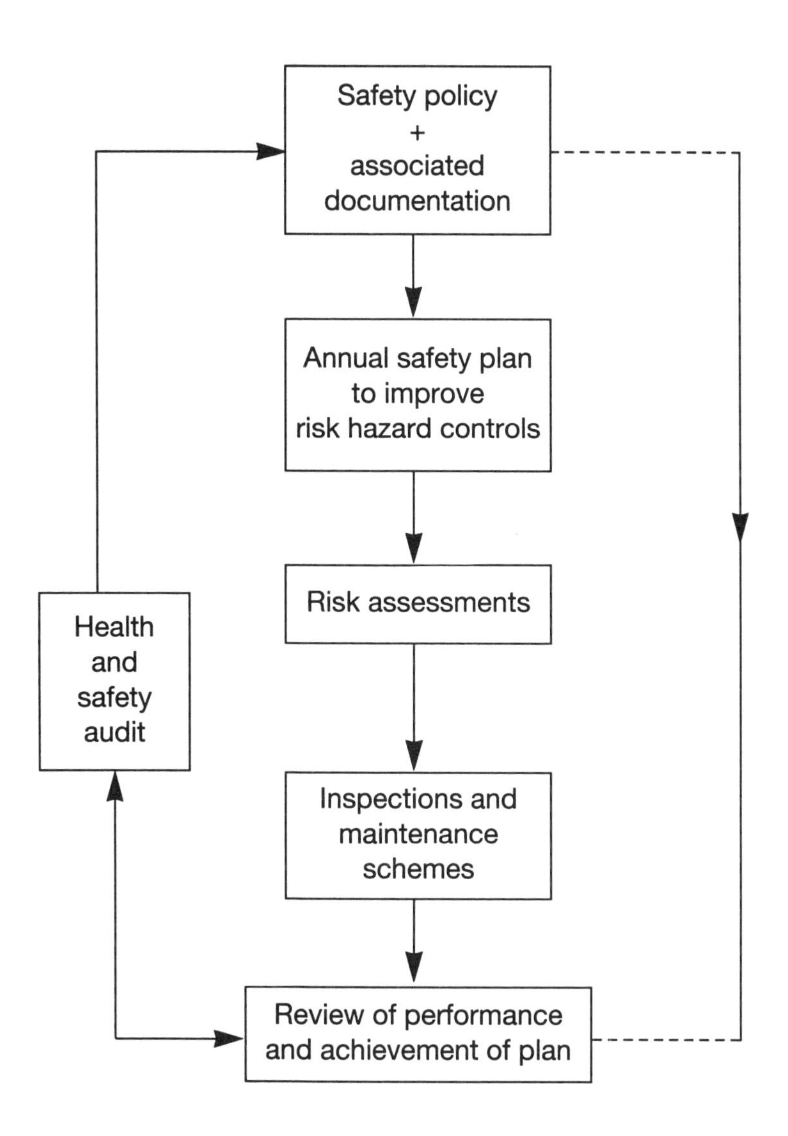

FIG 3.6 Risk assessment and health and safety management

Health risk assessments

Regulation 6 of the COSHH regulations 1994 places an absolute duty on an employer to make a suitable and sufficient assessment of the risks created by work that is liable to expose any employees to any substance hazardous to health (see Figure 4.1 (overleaf) and Chapter 1, The general and specific duties to assess risks).

IMPORTANT TERMINOLOGY

In order to make a 'suitable and sufficient' health risk assessment, it is essential that the person making the assessment is aware of some of the more significant definitions in the COSHH regulations and the Chemicals (Hazard Information and Packaging for Supply) Regulations 1994 (CHIP).

What is a 'substance hazardous to health'?

Regulation 2 of the COSHH regulations defines a substance hazardous to health as any substance (including any preparation) that is:

- listed in Part I of the *Approved Supply List* as dangerous for supply within the meaning of the CHIP regulations and for which an indication of danger specified for that substance in Part V of that list is very toxic, toxic, harmful, corrosive or irritant (see Table 4.1, pages 91–3)
- specified in Schedule 1 (which lists substances assigned *maximum exposure limits*) or for which the HSC has approved an *occupational exposure standard*

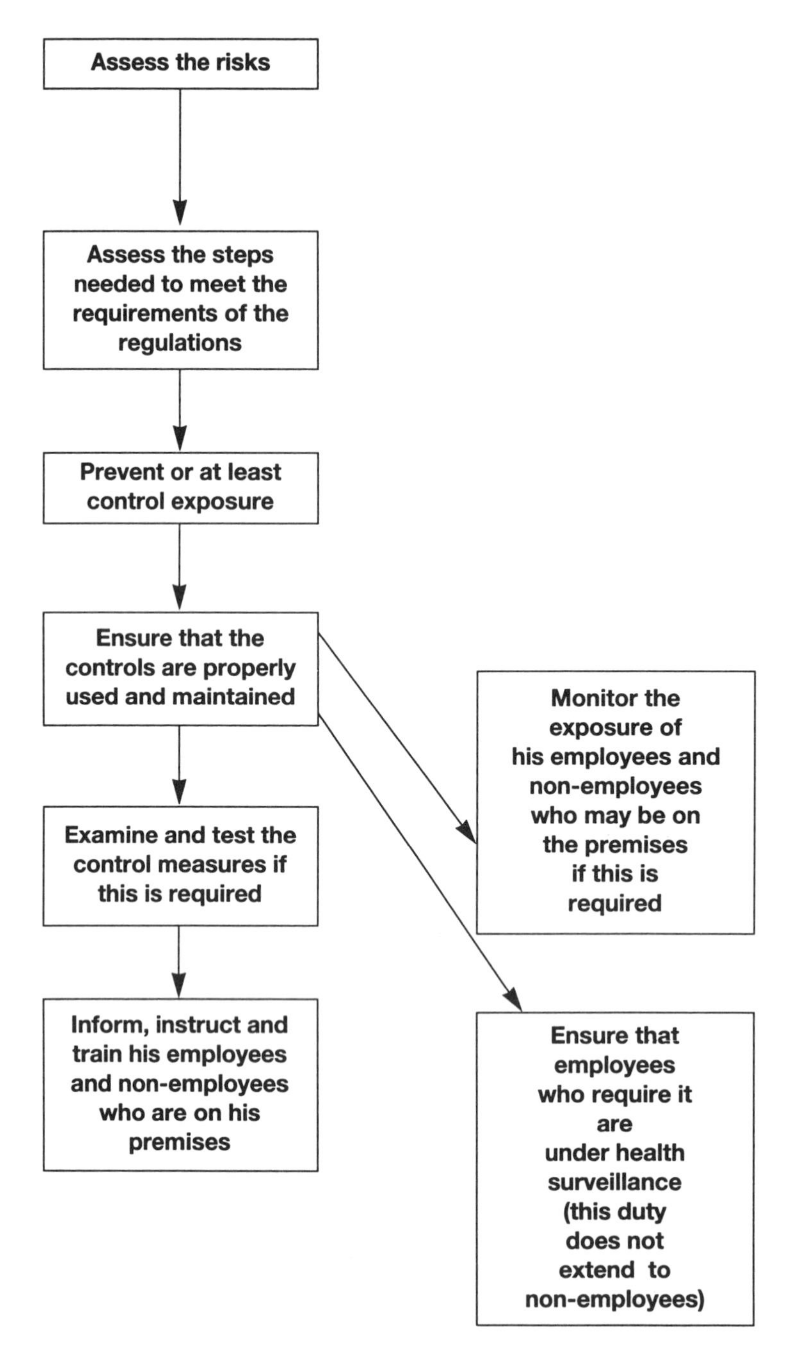

FIG 4.1 The main duties imposed on the employer by the COSHH regulations

- a *biological agent*
- *dust* of any kind, when present at a substantial concentration in air
- not one of the above, but which creates a hazard to the health of any person that is *comparable* with the hazards created by those substances.

The Approved Supply List

Regulation 4 of the CHIP regulations defines the *Approved Supply List* as meaning the list entitled *Approved Supply List: Information Approved for the Classification and Labelling of Substances and Preparations Dangerous for Supply* (2nd Edition) approved by the Health and Safety Commission on 18 October 1994 for the purposes of these regulations and comprising:

- in Part I:
  - in column 1, a list of the *names of the substances* for which the Commission has approved information
  - in the corresponding entries in columns 2 and 3 respectively the *index number* and (if any) the *CAS number* (for reference only) for the substance
- in Part II
  - in column 1, a list of the *index numbers* of the substances for which the Commission has approved information
  - in the corresponding entries in column 2 the *names* of those substances
- in Part III, a numbered list of the *risk phrases and combinations of risk phrases* the Commission has approved
- in Part IV, a numbered list of the *safety phrases and combinations of safety phrases* the Commission has approved
- in Part V, the *information* the Commission has approved for each substance referred to in Part I, namely:
  - in column 1, the *index number and abbreviated name* (for reference only)
  - in the corresponding entries in columns 2 to 4, respectively, the

classification, labelling data (including the EEC number) and any concentration limits the Commission has approved for the substance for the classification of *preparations* containing that substance

- in Part VI, a list of *conventional oral toxicity (LD_{50}) values* the Commission has approved in relation to *pesticides* for the purpose of classifying those pesticides in accordance with Schedule 4, together with such notes and explanatory material as are requisite for the use of the list.

Schedule 1 of Part I of the CHIP regulations is shown in Table 4.1.

What is a biological agent?

This means any micro-organism, cell culture or human endoparasite, including any that have been genetically modified, which may cause infection, allergy, toxicity or otherwise create a risk to human health.

What is a carcinogen?

This means:

- any substance or preparation classified in accordance with regulation 5 of the CHIP regulations would be in the category of danger, *carcinogenic (category 1) or carcinogenic (category 2)*, whether or not the substance or preparation would be required to be classified under those regulations
- any substance or preparation:
  - listed in *Schedule 8*
  - any substance or preparation arising from a *process* specified in *Schedule 8* that is hazardous to health.

What is a micro-organism?

This means a microbiological entity, cellular or non-cellular, that is capable of replication or of transferring genetic material.

Table 4.1 Classification of hazardous substances (supply requirements)

Hazardous substances are classified according to Schedule 1 of the Chemicals (Hazard Information and Packaging for Supply) Regulations 1994 as follows.

Part 1: Categories of danger		
Column 1 *Category of danger*	*Column 2* *Property (see note 1)*	*Column 3* *Symbol-letter*
Physico-chemical properties		
Explosive	Solid, liquid, pasty or gelatinous substances and preparations that may react exothermically without atmospheric oxygen, thereby quickly evolving gases and, under defined test conditions, detonate, quickly deflagrate or, on heating, explode when partially confined.	E
Oxidising	Substances and preparations that give rise to an exothermic reaction in contact with other substances, particularly flammable substances.	O
Extremely flammable	Liquid substances and preparations having an extremely low flash point and a low boiling point and gaseous substances and preparations that are flammable in contact with air at ambient temperature and pressure.	F+
Highly flammable	The following substances and preparations, namely: • substances and preparations that may become hot and finally catch fire in contact with air at ambient temperature without any application of energy • solid substances and preparations that may readily catch fire after brief contact with a source of ignition and continue to burn or be consumed after removal of the source of ignition • liquid substances and preparations having a very low flash point • substances and preparations that, in contact with water or damp air, evolve highly flammable gases in dangerous quantities (see note 2).	F
Flammable	Liquid substances and preparations having a low flash point.	None

Table 4.1 (Continued)

Column 1 Category of danger	*Column 2 Property (see note 1)*	*Column 3 Symbol-letter*
Health effects		
Very toxic	Substances and preparations that, in *very low* quantities, can cause death or acute or chronic damage to health when inhaled, swallowed or absorbed via the skin.	T+
Toxic	Substances and preparations that in *low quantities*, can cause death or acute or chronic damage to health when inhaled, swallowed or absorbed via the skin.	T
Harmful	Substances and preparations that may cause death or acute or chronic damage to health when inhaled, swallowed or absorbed via the skin.	Xn
Corrosive	Substances and preparations that, on contact, may *destroy* living tissues.	C
Irritant	Non-corrosive substances and preparations that through immediate, prolonged or repeated contact with the skin or mucous membrane, may cause *inflammation.*	Xi
Sensitising	Substances and preparations that, if they are inhaled or if they penetrate the skin, are capable of eliciting a reaction by *hypertension* such that on further exposure to the substance or preparation, characteristic adverse effects are produced.	
Sensitising by inhalation		Xn
Sensitising by skin contact		Xi
Carcino genic (see note 3)	Substances and preparations that, if they are inhaled or ingested or if they penetrate the skin, may induce *cancer* or increase its incidence.	
Category 1 Category 2 Category 3		T T Xn
Mutagenic (see note 3)	Substances and preparations that, if they are inhaled or ingested or if they penetrate the skin, may induce *heritable genetic defects* or increase their incidence.	

Column 1 *Category of danger*	*Column 2* *Property (see note 1)*	*Column 3* *Symbol-letter*
Category 1 Category 2 Category 3		T T Xn
Toxic for reproduction (see note 3)	Substances and preparations that, if they are inhaled or ingested or if they penetrate the skin, may produce or increase the incidence of *non-heritable* adverse effects in the progeny and/or an impairment of male or female reproductive functions or capacity.	
Category 1 Category 2 Category 3		T T Xn
Dangerous for the environment (see note 4)	Substances that, were they to enter into the environment, would present or might present an immediate or delayed danger for one or more components of the environment.	N

Notes

1 As further described in the *Approved Classification and Labelling Guide*.
2 Preparations packed in *aerosol dispensers* shall be classified as *flammable* in accordance with the additional criteria set out in Part II of this schedule.
3 The categories are specified in the *Approved Classification and Labelling Guide*.
4 Certain cases specified in the *Approved Supply List* and in the *Approved Classification and Labelling Guide* as *dangerous for the environment* are not required to be labelled with the symbol for this category of danger. This category of danger does not apply to preparations.

What is a maximum exposure limit?

The maximum exposure limit (MEL) for a substance hazardous to health means the maximum exposure limit for that substance set out in Schedule 1 in relation to the reference period specified there when calculated by a method approved by the HSC.

Regulation 7(6) of COSHH requires that where there is exposure to a substance for which an MEL is specified in Schedule 1, the control of exposure shall, so far as *inhalation* of the substance is concerned, only be treated as being adequate if the level of exposure is reduced so far as is reasonably practicable and, in any case, below the MEL.

What is an occupational exposure standard?

The occupational exposure standard (OES) for a substance hazardous to health means the standard approved by the HSC for that substance in relation to the specified reference period when calculated by a method approved by the HSC.

Regulation 7(7) of COSHH requires that where there is exposure to a substance for which an OES has been approved, the control of exposure shall, so far as *inhalation* of that substance is concerned, by treated as being adequate if:

- that OES is not exceeded
- where the OES is exceeded, the employer identifies the reasons for the standard being exceeded and takes appropriate action to remedy the situation as soon as is reasonably practicable.

HSE Guidance Note EH 40, *Occupational exposure limits*

Detailed information on the MELs and OESs for a wide range of substances hazardous to health are listed in the above HSE Guidance Note, which is reviewed on a regular basis.

ADDITIONAL FACTORS FOR CONSIDERATION

The *General COSHH ACOP* requires that, when considering whether or not a substance is hazardous to health, the following *additional* factors be taken into account:

- different *forms* of the same substance may present different hazards, so a solid may present a negligible hazard but when ground into dust of a respirable size, it may then be very hazardous
- many substances contain *impurities* that could present a greater hazard than the substance they contaminate, for example crystalline silica is often present in minerals that would otherwise present little or no hazard
- some substances have a *fibrous form* that may present a potentially serious hazard to health if the fibres are of a certain size or shape

- some substances may be known to cause ill health but the *causative agent* may not have been identified, such as certain textile dusts that cause byssinosis
- *combined or sequential exposures* to various substances may have additive or synergistic effects
- a *substantial concentration of dust* should be taken as a concentration of 10mg/m^3, 8-hour time-weighted average, of total *inhalable* dust or 5 mg/m^3, 8-hour time-weighted average, of *respirable* dust, where there is no indication of the need for a lower value (see current edition of HSE Guidance Note EH 40, *Occupational exposure limits*, for explanations of 'inhalable' and 'respirable' dust)
- epidemiological or other data indicating that a *biological agent* not already appearing in the *Approved Classification* is, nevertheless, the cause of a hazard to health at work.

SOURCES OF INFORMATION ON SUBSTANCES HAZARDOUS TO HEALTH

Sources of information about the hazardous properties of substances include:

- information on labels and safety data sheets complying with the CHIP regulations, or from classifying the substances by applying the criteria in the COSHH regulations
- information provided by the manufacturer or supplier of the substance under section 6 of the HSWA (amended by the Consumer Protection Act 1987)
- guidance material published by the HSE or other authoritative bodies
- experience obtained and information gathered as a result of previous use of the substance or similar substances
- technical reference sources (textbooks, scientific/technical papers, trade journals, etc.)
- professional institutions, trade associations, trade unions and specialist consultancy services.

THE HEALTH RISK ASSESSMENT PROCESS

As stated in Chapter 1, The general and specific duties to assess risks, the purpose of a health risk assessment is to enable a valid decision to be made about measures necessary to control substances hazardous to health arising from any work.

The principles of assessment

All substances hazardous to health can be managed safely provided that a suitable elimination or control strategy has been established and is operated effectively. Such a strategy incorporates four elements or phases:

- obtaining and passing on knowledge about the hazardous substance
- the assessment of hazards posed by the substance – in its use, storage and disposal and as by-products
- elimination or, where not practicable, control of the substances using recognised engineering techniques, safe operating procedures and PPE (see Figure 4.2)
- monitoring the effectiveness of the control strategy.

The five basic principles of occupational hygiene practice apply in this case, namely:

- *identify/recognise* the hazardous substance
- *measure* its concentration, particularly in air
- *evaluate* the results of measurement against known standards
- *control* the adverse effects of exposure to the substance
- *monitor* the controls installed to ensure their continuing effectiveness.

The COSHH regulations use the term 'assessment' in a very broad sense, encompassing not only the assessment of the hazards and risks involved, but also the subsequent development of control techniques applicable to the substance in question. A health risk assessment

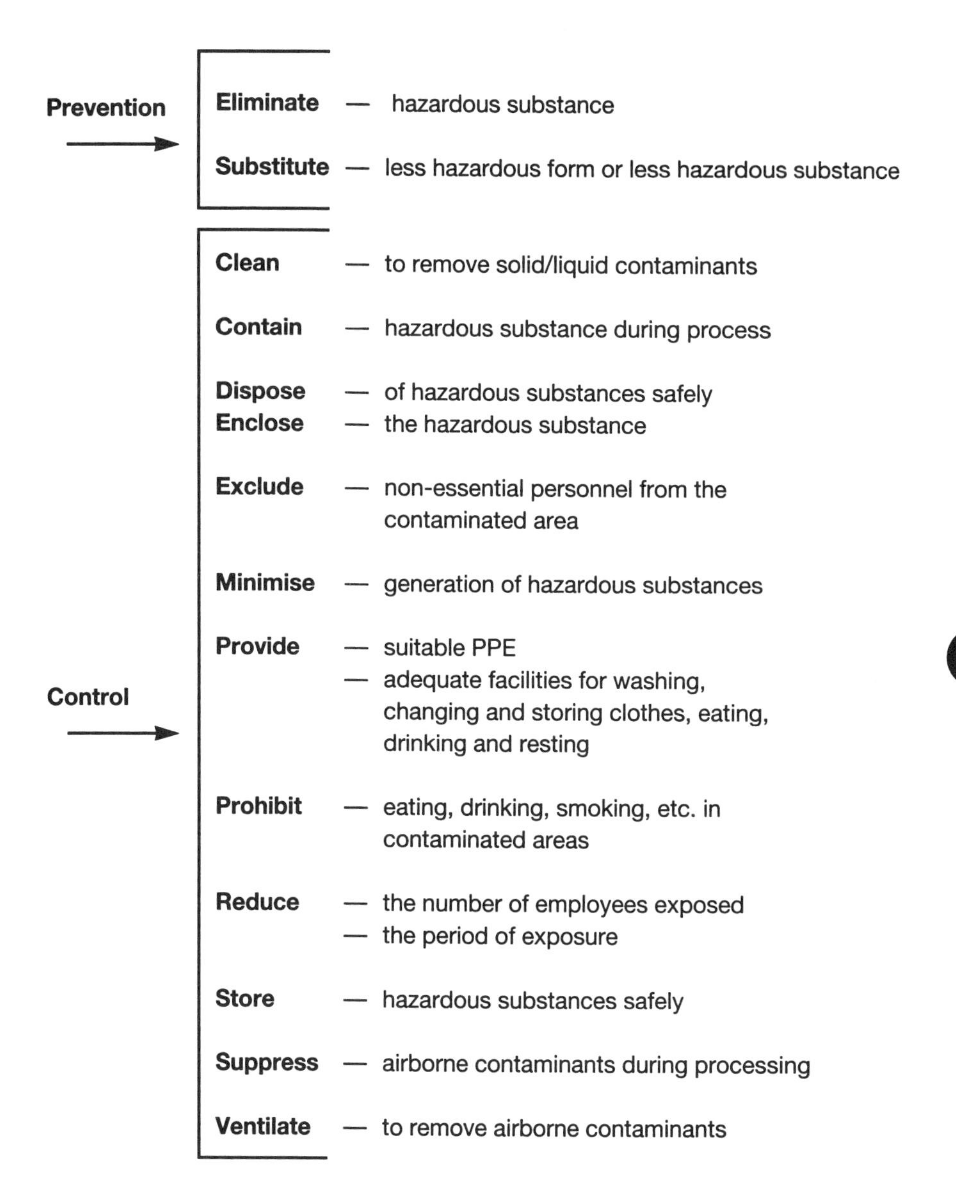

• **FIG 4.2 Measures for preventing or controlling exposure**

under the COSHH regulations can, therefore, be regarded as a written strategy sooner than a simple hazard and risk analysis.

Health risk assessment should take place in a number of clearly identified phases or stages.

Phase 1: obtaining and passing on knowledge

- Prepare lists of chemicals, substances and mixtures used, purchased, produced in the location or operation, to which employees and other people are otherwise exposed while at work.
- Consolidate the lists and prepare a matrix chart in tabular form indicating the substances and their uses.
- Gather information from suppliers, external data sources, industry associations, etc. on their properties, the hazards and risks arising.
- Summarise the basic hazards associated with each substance in the list.
- Prepare in-house data sheets to a common format.
- Inform, instruct and train employees and others in the actions necessary to reduce the risks.

Phase 2: assessment of risks in practice

- Assess each process or operation using the substances listed.
- Identify those substances defined in the COSHH regulations as being 'hazardous to health'.
- Review all substances and associated hazards on the list to identify further hazards or rule against unacceptable processes or practices.
- Assess the likely exposures to the substances listed, including any non-employees exposed to them.
- Compare these exposures with the appropriate occupational exposure limits, that is the MELs or OESs.
- Decide on the need for monitoring the air to assist with these last two points.

Phase 3: control of hazards and risks

For each substance, decide and record how it is to be controlled.

- Produce – or review existing – safe operating procedures in written form for each substance deemed to be hazardous to health, covering both processes and existing control measures.
- Ensure that specific reference is made to the appropriate PPE necessary by reference to the Personal Protective Equipment at Work

Regulations 1992 and HSE Guidance Notes (see further Chapter 8, Personal protective equipment risk assessments).

Phase 4: monitoring effectiveness

- Establish a procedure for reviewing existing control measures.
- Establish the frequency of required air monitoring as an on-going check of the effectiveness of control measures.
- Establish the necessary arrangements for maintenance, examination and testing of local exhaust ventilation (LEV) and other control measures.
- Establish procedures for supplying and maintaining PPE.
- Establish a procedure for incorporating newly acquired substances, new safety data information or changed work practices in the assessment.
- Establish the procedure for providing information, instruction and training to employees and others who may be exposed.
- Decide the frequency with which the assessment will be repeated in full or in part.
- Sign and date the finished assessment record, circulating copies to all interested and involved parties.

FEATURES OF A HEALTH RISK ASSESSMENT

A written health risk assessment should incorporate the following information:

- the *substances or types of substances* (including biological agents) employees are liable to be exposed to (taking into account the consequences of possible failure of any control measures provided to meet the requirements of regulation 7, such as local exhaust ventilation (LEV) systems)
- the *effects* these substances can have on the body
- the *potential location* of these substances and the *form* taken, such as gas, fumes, mist

- the *ways* in which and the *extent* to which any *groups* of employees or other people could potentially be exposed, taking into account the nature of the work and process and any reasonably foreseeable deterioration in, or failure of, any control measure provided for the purpose of regulation 7
- an *estimate of exposure*, taking into account engineering measures and systems of work currently employed for controlling potential exposure
- where *valid standards* exist, representing adequate control, comparison of the estimate with those standards
- *storage* requirements
- *air monitoring* requirements, where appropriate
- *first aid and health surveillance* requirements, where appropriate
- general *control* requirements, including those in the event of spillage and for disposal of waste
- *information, instruction and training* recommendations
- a general *conclusion* as to the risks entailed in the use of the substance in an identified activity or process and *recommendations* to ensure safe use.

These various features are considered below (for a summary, see Figure 4.3).

Hazardous substance details

This information should include the chemical name of the substance, any trade names, its chemical composition, the quantity in which it is supplied (such as 500 litres), labelling requirements, stated OESs (including short- and long-term exposure limits) and classification under the CHIP regulations.

Hazardous substances can be encountered in a variety of ways, for instance in the form of:

- raw materials for manufacturing or service processes, such as chemical feedstocks, solvents for degreasing or dry cleaning processes, paints, fertilisers for agricultural use, toners for dry copiers

1 Are hazardous substances likely to be present in the workplace?

- If no, no further action required.
- If yes, assessment required.

2 Gather information about the substances, the work and working practices.

- Decide who will carry out the assessment.
- What substances are present are are likely to be present?
- Identify the hazards.
- Find out who could be exposed to them.

3 Evaluate the risks to health

- *either* to the individual employees
- *or* on a group basis

Find out:

- the chance of exposure occurring
- what level of exposure could happen
- how long the exposure goes on for
- how often the exposure is likely to occur.

Conclude:

- *either* existing/potential exposure poses no significant risk
- *or* exposure poses significant risk.

4 Decide what needs to be done in terms of:

- controlling or preventing exposure
- maintaining controls
- using controls
- monitoring exposure
- health surveillance
- information, instruction and training.

5 Record the assessment.

- Decide if it is necessary to record the assessment.
- If it is necessary, decide:
  - what and how much to record
  - presentation and format.

6 Review the assessment.

Decide when review is needed.
Decide what needs to be reviewed.

Source: HSE

FIG 4.3 Summary of the COSHH assessment process

- engineering and cleaning materials, such as lubricants, cutting oils, water and effluent treatment chemicals, paints, toilet cleaners and bleaches
- in-service functions, such as adhesives, correcting fluids
- by-products of a process, such as *Legionella* organisms, exhaust fumes and gases.

The health risk assessment should identify the hazards and risks arising at the various stages of a process and in specific use situations as well as the control measures currently in place.

The form taken by a hazardous substance

The physical state of a substance is significant to its potential for harm, so this factor should be identified in the health risk assessment.

Hazardous substances come in many physical states, which can be classified as follows:

- *dusts* – these are solid airborne particles, often created by operations such as grinding, crushing, milling, sanding and demolition
- *fumes* – fumes are solid particles that usually form an oxide in contact with air and are created by industrial processes that involve the heating and melting of metals, such as welding, smelting and arc air gouging
- *smoke* – smoke is a product of incomplete combustion, mainly of organic materials, and may include fine particles of carbon in the form of ash, soot and grit that are visibly suspended in air
- *mists* – mists are finely dispersed liquids suspended in air, which are mainly created by spraying, foaming, pickling and electroplating processes – dangers arise most frequently from acid mists, such as chromic acid mist, produced in industrial treatment processes
- *gases* – these are formless fluids, usually produced by chemical processes involving combustion or by the interaction of chemical substances, and they will normally seek to fill the space completely into which they are liberated (certain gases, such as acetylene, hydrogen and methane, are particularly flammable, whereas other

gases, such as chlorine, may have an irritant effect and/or a toxic effect)

- *vapours* – a vapour is the gaseous form of a material normally encountered in a solid or liquid state at normal room temperature and pressure and typical examples are solvents, such as trichlorethylene, which release vapours when the container is opened, while other liquids produce a vapour on heating, the amount of vapour being directly related to the boiling point of that particular liquid (a vapour contains very minute droplets of the liquid, but in the case of a *fog*, the liquid droplets are much larger
- *solids* – certain substances in solid form can cause injury, for example cullet (broken glass), silica, asbestos and lead
- *liquids* – numerous dangerous substances are produced in liquid form, including acids, alkalis, caustic and acid-based detergents, solvents and fuels.

The effects of exposure

A health risk assessment should indicate the likely causes of exposure and the anticipated effect exposure would have on the human body. These effects include:

- *acute effect* – a rapidly produced effect following a single exposure to a substance hazardous to health
- *sub-acute effect* – a reduced form of acute effect
- *chronic effect* – an effect produced as a result of prolonged exposure or repeated exposures of long duration (the concentration of the offending agent may be low in both cases, but one single, prolonged exposure can result in chronic effects)
- *progressive chronic effect* – this continues to develop after exposure ceases
- *local effect* – this effect is generally confined to the initial point of contact, which may be the skin, mucous membranes of the eyes, nose or throat, liver, bladder, etc.
- *systemic effect* – these occur in parts of the body other than the initial

point of contact and are associated with a particular body system, such as the respiratory, circulatory or central nervous system.

Exposure to certain substances can also produce combined effects, such as an acute systemic effect.

Exposure situations – route(s) of entry

A very significant aspect of a health risk assessment is the route of entry taken into the body by the substance hazardous to health. Of particular importance are potential group exposure situations, perhaps as a result of unexpected incompatible reactions, adverse process reactions and unexpected by-product emissions from a process that could result in a gassing accident.

The principal route is inhalation, although substances can enter via pervasion, ingestion, injection, inoculation and implantation.

Inhalation

Inhalation of toxic substances in the form of dust, fumes, gas, vapour or mist accounts for the majority of deaths and illnesses associated with toxic substances. The results may be acute – as in the case of many gassing accidents, such as chlorine, carbon monoxide (at high concentrations), hydrogen sulphide and nitric oxide – or chronic (prolonged and cumulative) – as with exposure to, for example, chlorinated hydrocarbons, lead compounds, dusts that lead to pneumoconiosis, mists and fogs, such as oil mist and paint sprays, and fumes, notably from welding operations.

Pervasion

The skin, if intact, is proof against most but not all inputs. There are certain substances and micro-organisms that are capable of passing straight through the intact skin into underlying tissue or even into the bloodstream without apparently causing any change in the skin itself (*percutaneous effect*). The resistance of the skin to external irritants varies with age, sex, race, colour and, to a certain extent, diet.

Pervasion, as a route of entry, is normally associated with occupational dermatitis, the causes of which may broadly be divided into two groups. *Primary irritants* are substances that will cause dermatitis at the site of contact if permitted to act for sufficient length of time in sufficient concentrations, as is the case with strong acids, alkalis and solvents. *Secondary cutaneous sensitisers*, on the other hand, do not necessarily cause skin changes, but effect a specific sensitisation of the skin. If further contact occurs after an interval of approximately seven or more days, dermatitis will develop at the site of the second contact. Examples of secondary cutaneous sensitisers are some rubber additives, certain wood dusts and proteolytic enzymes.

Ingestion

Certain substances are carried into the intestine and there some will pass into the body by pervasion through the intestinal wall. Like the lung, the intestine behaves as a selective filter, keeping out many, but not all, harmful agents presented to it.

Injection, inoculation and implantation

A forceful breach of the skin, perhaps as a result of injury, can carry harmful substances through the skin barrier.

Estimating the potential for exposure

Depending on the substance involved, its use in a process, the MEL/OES, current engineering controls, systems of work and the ongoing use of PPE, it should be possible to predict and estimate the exposure potential for a substance hazardous to health, together with those groups who could suffer exposure.

Comparison with existing standards

Current standards are those quoted in HSE Guidance Note EH 40, *Occupational exposure limits*, in Schedule 1 of the COSHH regulations and by other authoritative organisations, such as the International Labour Organisation (ILO) and the American Conference of Government Industrial Hygienists (ACGIH).

Storage requirements

The system and arrangements for safe storage – including temperatures, maximum quantities and incompatible situations, such as where storage with other substances could be dangerous – should be specified in the health risk assessment.

Air monitoring

The assessment should indicate, where appropriate, situations where air monitoring is recommended, the particular technique to be used, such as static sampling, and the standard for evaluation.

First aid and health surveillance

First aid procedures in event of skin contact, ingestion, inhalation and eye contact should be specified, along with recommended health surveillance procedures, such as six-monthly health examinations, urine tests or lung function tests.

General controls including waste disposal and spillage control

Any general control methods, such as the use of LEV systems, safe handling systems and the use of PPE, should be specified. Where substances may also be flammable, an indication of the type of fire appliance to be used in combatting a fire should be specified. Procedures for the disposal of contaminated waste, perhaps through a licensed waste disposal contractor, should further be specified, together with methods to control spillages, such as containment and the use of neutral absorbent compounds.

Information, instruction and training requirements

Procedures for ensuring awareness to risks on the part of those handling the substance should be incorporated, together with the responsibilities of supervisory management in terms of regular briefing of users in safe handling procedures. Training requirements should be specified for all potential users, covering induction, change of process and use of the substance.

General conclusion

The conclusion to the risk assessment should indicate the principal hazards, the risks involved and an indication of the level of risk – whether it is high, medium or low – relating to the specific use of the substance.

A typical layout for a health risk assessment under the regulations is shown in Figure 4.4 (overleaf).

HEALTH RISK ASSESSMENT
Control of Substances Hazardous to Health Regulations 1994

Assesment no.	
Location	*Process/activity/use*
Substance information	
Name of substance	*Chemical composition and formula*
Supplier	
Risk information	
Risk classification	*Stated occupational exposure limits*
	MEL/OES
	LTEL STEL
Route(s) of entry	*Effects of exposure*
	Acute
Exposure situations	Chronic
	Local
Estimate of potential exposure	Systemic
Frequency of use	*Quantities used*
Duration of use	
Storage requirements	

● **FIG 4.4 Example of a health risk assessment form**

Air monitoring requirements and standards

First aid requirements

Health surveillance requirements

Disposal requirements

Procedure in the event of spillage

1 Large-scale spillage

2 Small-scale spillage

Information, instruction and training arrangements

General conclusions as to risk

High/medium/low risk

Special precautions

Supervision requirements

Date for reassessment

Assessor *Date*

4

FIG 4.4 (Continued)

Noise risk assessments

SOUND AND NOISE

Sound is defined as any pressure variation in air, water or some other medium that the human ear can detect. Within the physical sense, sound is a vibration of particles in a gas, liquid or solid.

Noise is generally defined as 'unwanted sound'. Noise can:

- be a nuisance, resulting in various forms of stress and, as such, may be actionable under the *Environmental Protection Act 1989*
- distract attention and concentration, mask audible warning signals or interfere with work, thereby being a causative factor in accidents
- result in hearing impairment.

SOURCES OF NOISE

Noise in the working environment can include the following:

- noise produced as a result of vibration in machines
- noise taking a structure-borne pathway
- radiation of structural vibration into the air
- turbulence created by air or gas flow
- noise taking an airborne pathway
- noise produced by vibratory hand tools, such as chainsaws and angle grinders.

In the assessment of noise, not only must the source of the noise be considered but also the pathway it takes to the recipient.

THE EFFECTS OF EXPOSURE TO NOISE

The most common condition associated with exposure to noise is occupational deafness. Under the provisions of the *Social Security (Industrial Injuries) (Prescribed Diseases) Regulations 1985*, the condition is described as follows:

> Substantial sensorineural hearing loss amounting to at least 50 dB in each ear, being due in the case of at least one ear to occupational noise and being the average of pure tone losses measured by audiometry over the 1, 2 and 3 KHz frequencies.

It must be recognised that part of the normal ageing process for many people is a reduction in the ability to hear. It is important to distinguish between *presbycusis* (age-induced deafness) and *sociocusis* (occupational deafness). An audiogram will indicate this difference.

Exposure to noise may affect hearing in the following three ways.

Temporary threshold shift

This is the short-term effect – that is, a temporary reduction in hearing acuity (temporary deafness) that may follow exposure to noise. The condition is reversible and very much depends on individual susceptibility to noise.

Permanent threshold shift

This takes place where the limit of tolerance is exceeded in terms of time, the level of noise and individual susceptibility. Recovery from permanent threshold shift will not proceed to completion, but will effectively cease at some particular point in time after the end of the exposure. The term 'permanent threshold shift' is reserved for conditions that may be reasonably supposed to have no possibility of further recovery.

Acoustic trauma

Acoustic trauma involves sudden aural damage resulting from short-term intense exposure or even from one single exposure. Explosive pressure rises are often responsible, such as exposure to gunfire, major explosions or even fireworks.

SOUND INTENSITY, SOUND PRESSURE LEVEL AND FREQUENCY

In order to assess the risks from exposure to noise, it is important to distinguish between *sound intensity, sound pressure level* and *frequency.*

Sound intensity

This describes the particular power of a sound or the level of energy of a sound as it confronts the ear. Intensity describes the rate of flow of sound energy. Thus, high-intensity sound has more energy than low-intensity sound.

Sound pressure level

Sound intensity is difficult to measure directly, but the passage of sound energy through air is accompanied by fluctuations in atmospheric pressure. These fluctuations can be measured and related to the amount of sound energy that is flowing. Therefore, it is usual to measure sound pressure level, which is a measurement of the magnitude of the air pressure variations or fluctuations that make up sound. The root mean square value of the pressure variations is used and expressed in *decibels (dB).*

Frequency

Frequency is the number of complete pressure variations passing a fixed point per second. It is measured in *hertz (Hz),* and 1 Hz = 1 cycle per second and 1 KHz = 1000 cycles per second. The frequency of a sound gives it its distinguishing character. For instance, high-frequency sound, such as a train whistle, will sound high-pitched, whereas low-frequency sound, such as that from a double bass, will sound low-pitched. The more rapidly the vibrations occur, the higher is the frequency and vice versa.

The decibel scale

It is important to recognise that the decibel scale is a logarithmic, not a linear scale. A sound pressure level meter measures sound intensity on a comparative basis. The range of intensities to which the ear responds, however, is enormous from the *threshold of hearing* to the *threshold of pain*. For example, at 1 KHz, the threshold of pain is 100 000 000 000 000 (10^{14}) times more intense that the threshold of hearing, where sound is just discernible. It is clearly difficult to express such ratios on a simple arithmetic scale, so a logarithmic scale is used, which has the effect of compressing that scale. The standard unit is the *bel*. However, this is a very large unit and is thus divided into tenths, giving *decibels*.

Sound is further measured on the A network of a sound pressure level meter, which is the network that most closely relates to the performance of the human ear. Hence the use of the term decibels(A) (dB(A)), indicating decibels measured on the A network of a sound pressure level meter.

The use of a logarithmic scale in sound measurement has a further advantage, because the evaluation of intensities is simplified by the replacement of multiplication with addition and of division with subtraction. Furthermore, the response of the ear tends to follow a logarithmic scale.

The addition of decibels is carried out on a ratio basis, rather than an arithmetic one, and Table 5.1 may be used to simplify the procedure. To add two sound pressure levels, take the difference between the two levels and add the corresponding figure in the right-hand column to the higher sound pressure level.

Table 5.1 The addition of decibels

Difference (dB)	*Add to higher (dB)*
0.0–0.5	3.0
1.0–1.5	2.5
2.0–3.0	2.0
3.5–4.5	1.5
5.0–7.0	1.0
7.5–12.0	0.5
Over 12.0	0.0

Pascals

Under the SI system, sound pressure is expressed in pascals. A pascal is a unit of pressure corresponding to a force of one newton acting uniformly on an area of 1 square metre. Hence, $1 \text{ Pa} = 1 \text{ N/m}^2$.

NOISE AT WORK REGULATIONS 1989

The duty of employers to assess exposure to noise is detailed in regulation 4 of these regulations, with guidance on the process being given in *Noise Guide No. 1: Legal duties of employers to prevent damage to hearing* (see further Chapter 1, The general and specific duties to assess risks).

NOISE RISK ASSESSMENTS

Regulation 4 requires that every employer shall, when any of his employees is likely to be exposed to the *first action level* (a daily personal noise exposure of 85 dB(A)) or above or to the *peak action level* (a level of peak sound pressure of 200 pascals) or above, ensure that a competent person makes a noise assessment that is adequate for the purposes. The formulae for assessing noise exposure are given in the Schedule to the regulations:

- Part I states the formula for assessing the daily personal noise exposure of employees

- Part II states the formula for assessing the weekly average of daily personal noise exposure of employees.

These are shown in Figures 5.1 and 5.2 (overleaf), respectively.

Noise exposure records

On completion of the assessment, the exposure should be recorded using a form set out like that shown in Figure 5.3 (overleaf).

Action required

Details of the action required under the regulations according to measured sound pressure levels is summarised in Table 5.2.

Table 5.2 The action levels specified under the Noise at Work Regulations 1989

Action required where Lep.d is likely to be: (see note 1 below)	*below 84 dB(A)*	*85 dB(A) 1st AL*	*90 dB(A) 2nd AL*
EMPLOYER'S DUTIES **General duty to reduce risk** Risk of hearing damage to be reduced to the lowest level.	●	●	(2) ●
Assessment of noise exposure Noise assessments to be made by a competent person (reg.4). Record of assessments to be kept until a new one is made (reg. 5)		● ●	● ●
Noise reduction Reduce exposure to noise as far as is reasonably practicable by means other than ear protectors (reg. 7).			●
Provision of information to workers Provide adequate information, instruction and training about risks to hearing, what employees should do to minimise risk, how they can obtain ear protectors if they are exposed between 85 and 90dB(A), and their obligations under the regulations (reg. 11). Mark ear protection zones and notices, so far as reasonably practicable (reg. 9).		●	● ●

Action required where Lep.d is likely to be: (see note 1 below)	*below 84 dB(A)*	*85 dB(A) 1st AL*	*90 dB(A) 2nd AL*
Ear protectors Ensure, so far as is practicable, that protectors are:			
● provided to employees who ask for them (reg. 8(1))		●	●
● provided to all exposed (reg. 8(2))		●	●
● maintained and repaired (reg. 10(1)(b))			●
● used by all exposed (reg. 10(1)(a)).			●
Ensure, so far as reasonably practicable, that all who go into a marked ear protection zone use ear protectors (reg. 9 (1) (b)).			(3)
Maintenance and use of equipment Ensure so far as is practicable, that:			
● all equipment provided under the regulations is used, except for the ear protectors provided between 85 and 90 dB(A) (reg. 10(1)(a))		●	●
● ensure all equipment is maintained (reg. 10(1)(b)).		●	●
EMPLOYEE'S DUTIES **Use of equipment** So far as practicable:			
● use ear protectors (reg. 10(2))			●
● use any other protective equipment (reg. 10(2))		●	●
● report any defects discovered to his/her employer (reg. 10(2)).		●	●
MACHINE MAKERS' AND SUPPLIERS' DUTIES **Provision of information** Provide information on the noise likely to be generated (reg. 12).		●	●

Notes: *(1) The dB(A) action levels are values of daily personal exposure to noise ($L_{EP,d}$).*
(2) All the actions indicated at 90 dB(A) are also required where the peak sound pressure is above 200 Pa (140 dB re 20 μPa).

5

THE SCHEDULE

Regulations
2(1) and 13(1)

PART I
DAILY PERSONAL NOISE EXPOSURE OF EMPLOYEES

The daily personal noise exposure of an employee ($L_{EP.d}$) is expressed in dB(A) and is ascertained using the formula:

$$L_{EP.d} = 10 \log_{10} \left\{ \frac{1}{T_0} \int_0^{T_e} \left[\frac{P_A(t)}{P_0} \right]^2 dt \right\}$$

where:
T_e = the duration of the person's personal exposure to sound
T_0 = 8 hours = 28,800 seconds
p_0 = 20 μPa
$P_A(t)$ = the time-varying value of A – weighted instantaneous sound pressure in pascals in the undisturbed field in air at atmospheric pressure to which the person is exposed (in the locations occupied during the day) or the pressure of the disturbed field adjacent to the person's head adjusted to provide a notional equivalent undisturbed field pressure.

● **FIG 5.1 The formula for assessing the daily personal noise exposure of employees**

PART II
WEEKLY AVERAGE OF DAILY PERSONAL NOISE EXPOSURE OF EMPLOYEES

The weekly average of an employee's daily personal noise exposure ($L_{EP.w}$) is expressed in dB(A) and is ascertained using the formula:

$$L_{EP.w} = 10 \log_{10} \left[\frac{1}{5} \sum_{k=1}^{k=m} 10^{0.1(L_{EP.d})_k} \right]$$

where:
$(L_{EP.d})_k$ = the values of $L_{EP.d}$ for each of the m working days in the week being considered.

● **FIG 5.2 The formula for assessing the weekly average of daily personal noise exposure of employees**

NOISE EXPOSURE RECORD

Name and address of premises, department, etc. ______________________________

____

____

____

Date of survey ________________ *Survey made by* ______________________________

Workplace and number of persons	*Noise level (Leq(s) or sound level)*	*Daily exposure period*	$L_{EP.d}$ *dB(a)*	*Peak pressure (where appropriate)*	*Comments/ remarks*

General comments ____

Instruments used ____

Date of last calibration ______________________ *Signature* ____________________

Date ____________________

● **FIG 5.3 Example of a noise exposure record**

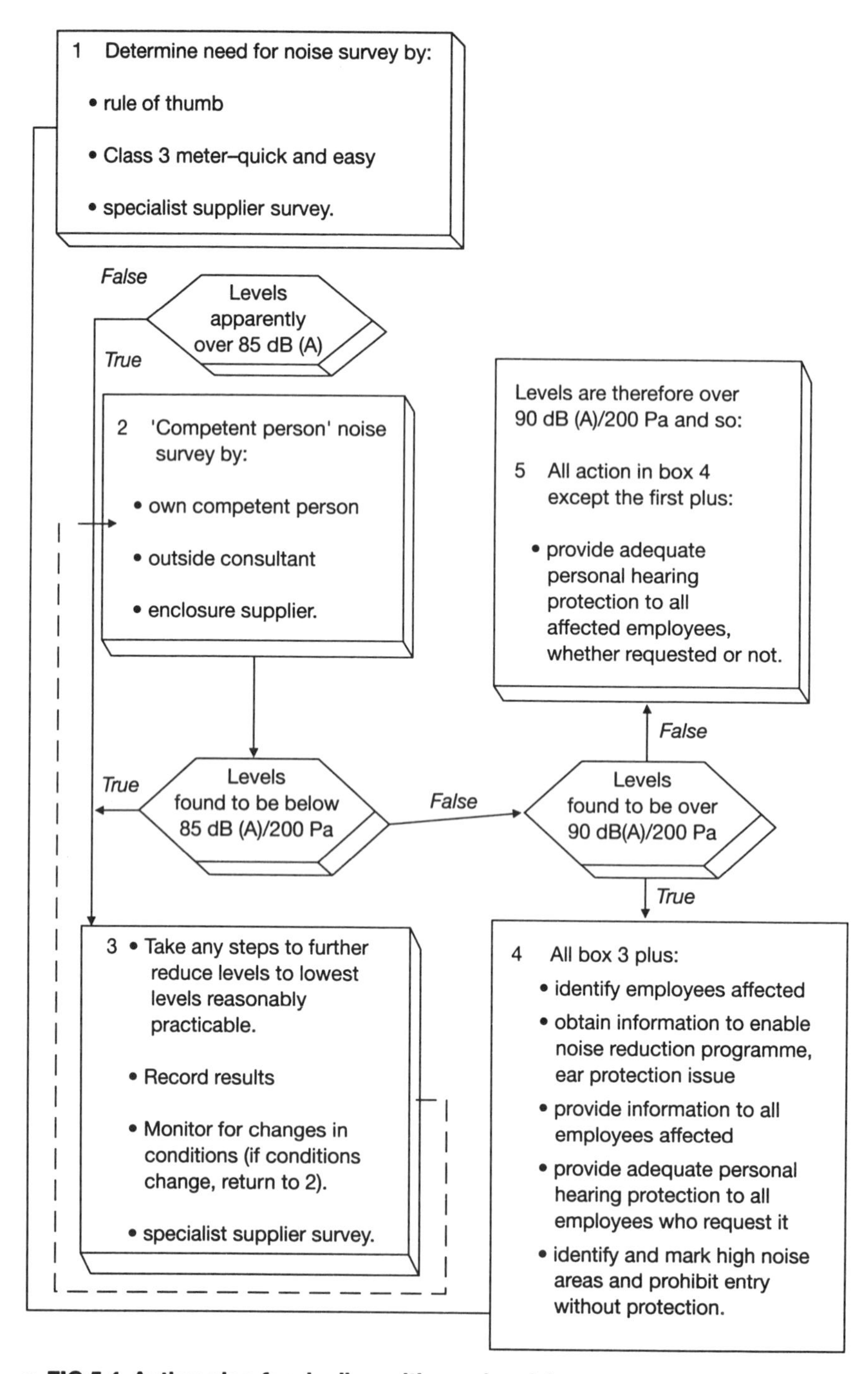

FIG 5.4 Action plan for dealing with a noise risk assessment

Action plans for dealing with noise

A step-by-step action plan for dealing with the various stages of a noise risk assessment is shown in Figure 5.4.

Noise control programmes

It should be recognised that the process of noise control in the workplace should be undertaken on a structured basis, commencing with an initial noise survey, through exposure assessment and frequency analysis to the implementation of various protection strategies. This should be followed by charting of the overall noise situation and the preparation of a hearing conservation plan. Such plan may incorporate hearing tests (audiometry), the provision of information, instruction and training to affected employees and the implementation of hearing conservation measures. As with any programme, it should be reviewed at regular intervals to ensure satisfactory progress and the incorporation of any revisions to the programme in the light of experience. A typical structure for a noise control programme is shown in Figure 5.5 (overleaf).

Noise assessment summary

The process of noise assessment is summarised in Figure 5.6 (overleaf).

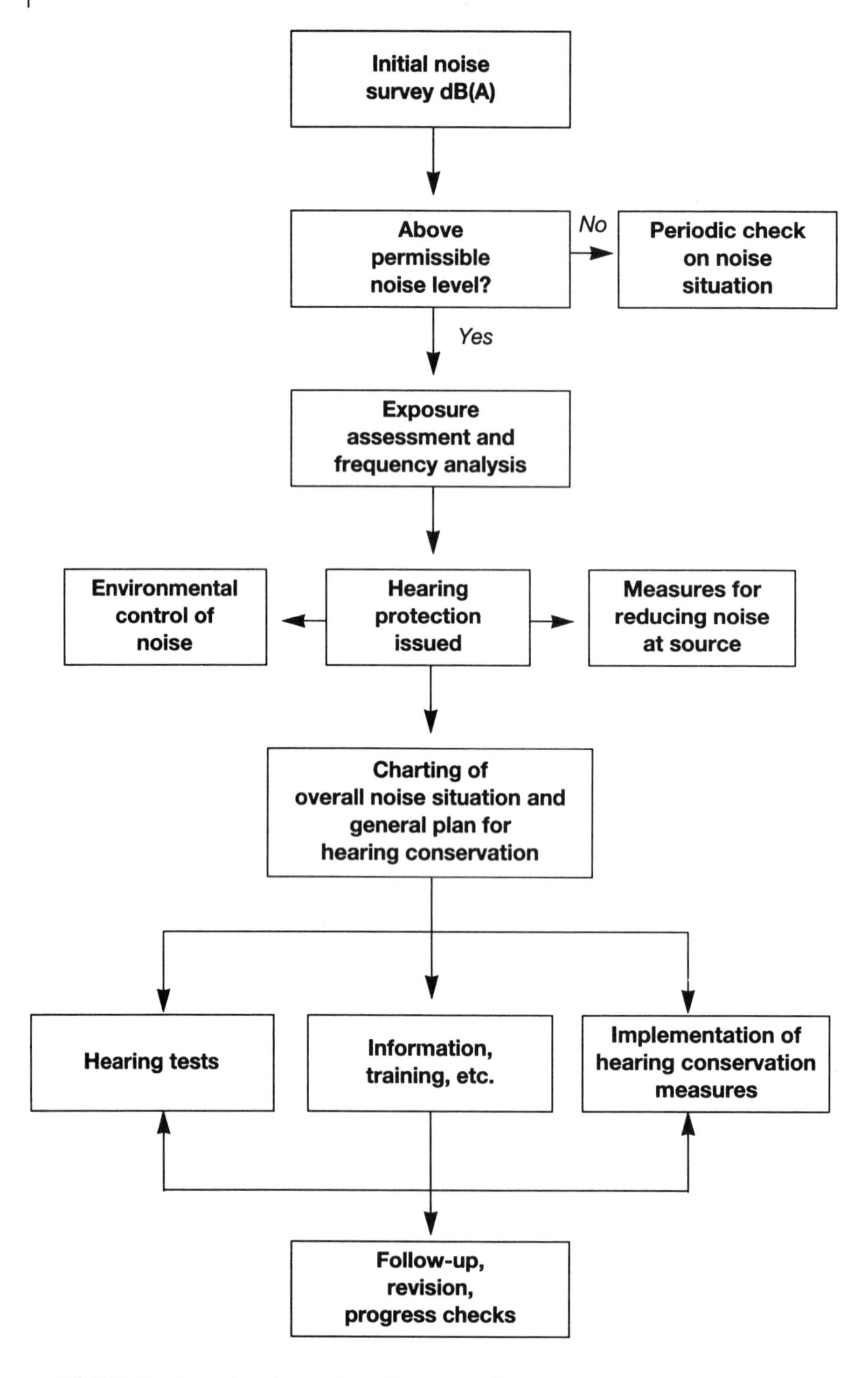

FIG 5.5 Typical structure of a noise control programme

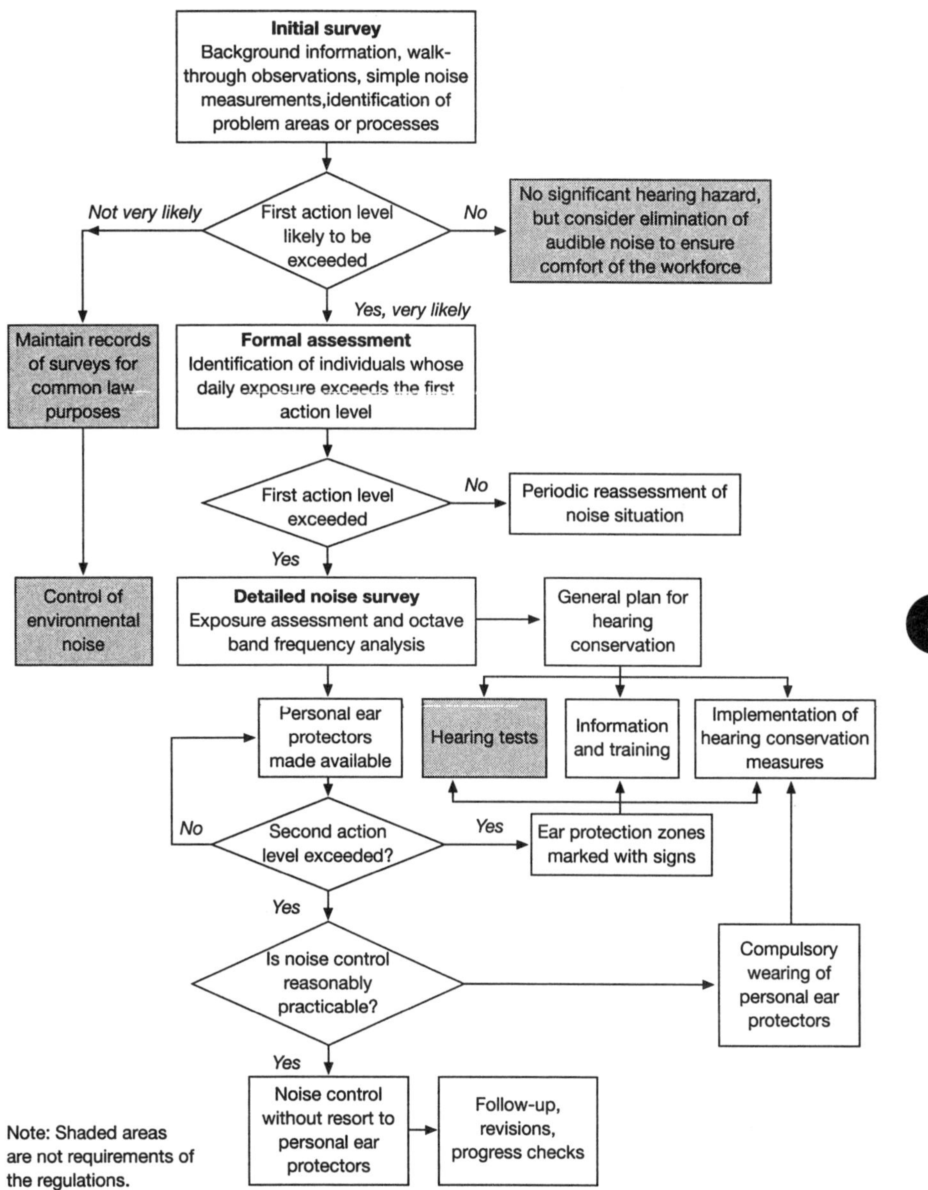

5

• **FIG 5.6 Flow chart for assessment under the Noise at Work Regulations 1989**

Workplace and work activity risk assessments

Regulation 3 of the MHSWR places a general duty on employers to assess the risks to workers and others who may be affected by their 'undertaking'. An undertaking can be the operation of a series of processes in a specific *workplace*, such as a workshop, factory, office or construction site, or the carrying out of certain *activities*, such as window cleaning, servicing and maintenance of equipment, in the same or different locations. An employer must consider, therefore, whether a workplace risk assessment – or a series of work activity risk assessments or both – is more appropriate to meet the requirements of these regulations, taking into account the relevant statutory provisions that apply to his undertaking.

WORKPLACE RISK ASSESSMENTS

Where an organisation operates a series of workplaces of a similar nature in terms of construction, layout and operations – such as a chain of shops, offices, transport maintenance units or retail distribution depots – it may be appropriate to undertake a model or generic risk assessment. On the other hand, where the activities in a workplace are highly specialised and with particular risks and/or where the layout and construction are unique, a specific workplace risk assessment is required.

The term 'workplace' is very broadly defined in the *Workplace (Health, Safety and Welfare) Regulations 1992 (WHSWR)* as meaning any premises, or part of a premises, that are not domestic premises and are made available to anyone as a place of work. This includes:

- any place within the premises to which such a person has access while at work
- any room, lobby, corridor, road or other place used as a means of access to or egress from the workplace or where facilities are provided for use in connection with the workplace other than a public road.

Identifying the hazards

Carrying out a workplace risk assessment takes place in a number of clearly defined stages. The first stage of the exercise is the undertaking of some form of safety monitoring, such as a safety inspection or audit. This should identify the hazards, which can then be classified, for instance, as structural hazards, environmental hazards, those relating to access and egress, fire, welfare amenity provisions, maintenance and security arrangements.

The second stage is to identify those relevant statutory provisions that apply to the workplace in question, such as the Ionising Radiations Regulations 1985 and the Provision and Use of Work Equipment Regulations 1992. Other information of relevance at this stage is the past history of injuries and ill health arising from the workplace and the operations carried out there.

Measuring and evaluating the risks

From this information, the risks can then be measured and evaluated. This can entail a basic quantitative approach to produce risk ratings, such as that described in Chapter 3, The risk assessment process, under probability, severity and frequency. This enables the risks to be ranked according to significance.

Remedial action

Once the risks have been ranked, the remedial action can be considered and priorities allocated. The remedial action should be recorded on the risk assessment summary (see the examples of risk assessment documentation given in Figures 3.4a to d). Other matters that should be recorded include the information, instruction, training and any supervisory requirements. The date of the next review should be incorporated into the summary, which should be signed by the individual making the assessment.

FACTORS FOR CONSIDERATION IN A WORKPLACE RISK ASSESSMENT

The requirements of the WHSWR provide an indication of the factors that must be considered in a workplace risk assessment. It may be necessary, however, to consider other legislation, ACOPs and Guidance Notes that may apply generally or specifically to the workplace in question. These factors are outlined below, indicating the key points for consideration in the assessment.

Maintenance arrangements

Maintenance

This means the state of maintenance of structure, equipment, devices and systems, state of cleanliness and the operation of a planned preventative maintenance system, including that for mechanical ventilation systems.

Environmental factors

Ventilation

Whether or not effective and suitable natural and, where necessary, mechanical ventilation, exists and whether or not there are effective devices to warn of mechanical ventilation plant failure.

Temperature control

A reasonable, comfortable temperature should be maintained according to tasks and occupancy and suitable PPE and rest facilities should be provided for low-temperature working. There should be temporary heating arrangements, maintenance of fixed heating systems, control of fume emission from portable heaters, and thermometers should be installed.

Lighting

There should be suitable and sufficient lighting, emergency lighting provision, elimination of glare, suitably located switches, light fittings should not be obscured, specific task lighting should exist where needed and windows and skylights should be clean and free from obstructions.

Cleanliness and waste materials

Structural surfaces, furniture, furnishings and fittings should be kept clean; the surfaces of floors, walls and ceilings should be capable of being kept clean; and a cleaning schedule and control over accumulations of waste should exist.

Room dimensions and space

Look for evidence of overcrowding.

Workstations and seating

Workstations should be suitable for the individuals and the nature of the work undertaken. Outdoor workstations should be protected from adverse weather and designed to allow swift egress and be free from slipping, tripping and falling hazards. Suitable seats should be provided, plus footrests.

Structural features

Floors and traffic routes

These should be of a suitable construction, free from dangerous holes, slopes, uneven or slippery surfaces. There should be effective drainage, where necessary and they should be free from obstructions, articles and substances that could cause slips, trips or falls. Handrails and/or guards should be provided where necessary.

Falls and falling objects

Suitable and effective measures should be in place to prevent people falling and coming into contact with falling objects. Dangerous tanks, pits and structures should be securely covered or fenced off, and traffic routes over, across or in uncovered tanks, pits or structures should, likewise, be securely fenced off. Fixed ladders should be sound, extended at landings, with resting places installed every 6 metres, and fitted with safety hoops. Roof edge protection should be provided in cases of flat roofs. Changes of floor level should be marked. Materials should be safely stacked and stored. There should be safe access for vehicle loading and unloading. Fall arrest systems, or safety lines and harnesses with secure anchorage points, should be provided where appropriate.

Windows and transparent or translucent doors, gates and walls

These should be fitted with safety material or protected against breakage and suitably marked where necessary.

Windows, skylights and ventilators

These should be safe to open, close or adjust, safe when open and devices fitted to limit opening where necessary.

Ability to clean windows, etc. safely

Windows and skylights should be designed or constructed to permit safe cleaning, access equipment should be provided and used and anchorage points for safety harnesses fitted.

Organisation of traffic routes

There should be safe circulation for pedestrians and vehicles with a sufficient number of traffic routes suitable for people or vehicles in suitable positions, of sufficient size and suitably indicated.

Doors and gates

These should be suitably constructed. Sliding upward-opening, powered and two-way-opening doors and gates should be fitted with the necessary safety devices.

Escalators and moving walkways

These should function safely, be equipped with the necessary safety devices and fitted with one or more emergency stops.

Welfare amenity provisions

Sanitary conveniences

There should be suitable and sufficient toilets, located at readily accessible places. They should be adequately ventilated and lit, in a clean and orderly condition and there should be a separation of the sexes.

Washing facilities

These should be suitable and sufficient, showers being provided according to the nature of the work, and located at readily accessible places in the immediate vicinity of sanitary conveniences and changing rooms. There should be hot and cold water, soap, etc. and drying facilities. The rooms should be sufficiently ventilated, in a clean and orderly condition and there should be a separation of the sexes.

Drinking water

There should be an adequate and wholesome supply with cups or other drinking vessels provided where the water is not from a jet.

Accommodation for clothing

Suitable and sufficient facilities should be provided for personal clothing not worn during working hours and special work clothing, with security arrangements for personal clothing, and separate accommodation for personal and work clothing where necessary. There should also be facilities for drying clothing and all facilities should be suitably located.

Facilities for changing clothing

These should be suitable and sufficient and afford adequate privacy and segregation of the sexes.

Facilities to rest and eat meals

There should be suitable and sufficient rest facilities in readily accessible places with specific rest rooms or rest areas provided. There should be facilities to eat meals where there is a risk of contamination to food, segregation of smokers from non-smokers, facilities for pregnant women or nursing mothers to rest, and for eating meals where meals are regularly eaten in the workplace.

Fire protection

There should be means of escape in the event of fire, fire drill arrangements, adequate and suitable fire appliances and equipment, heat and smoke detectors installed, one or more fire alarms that are operational and tested, fire instructions displayed and an emergency lighting system.

Emergency procedure

There should be a formally established procedure, with competent persons appointed to implement it and controlled areas established.

Vehicle movements

There should be segregation of pedestrian and vehicular traffic movement areas, designated parking and loading/unloading areas, an operational one-way system, adequate road markings and signs, 'no go' areas marked, speed controls in force, speed ramps installed, pedestrian crossings marked, convex mirrors installed at obscured junctions and fork-lift truck routes marked.

Electrical installations and appliances

Electrical systems should be maintained, there should be written procedures for the safe operation, use and maintenance of equipment in operation, procedures for adverse or hazardous environments, equipment should be adequately protected from rain, weather, dusty or corrosive, etc. conditions, connections should be mechanically suitable, there should be insulation of conductors and earthing or other suitable means to prevent danger, precautions should be in place for work near live conductors and means for protecting from excess current and cutting off supply and isolation, competent persons should be appointed, installations and portable tools examined and tested, there should be flameproof equipment, PPE and training procedures.

Information, instruction, training and supervision

Information on hazards and precautions should be available, instruction should be provided, as well as arrangements made for induction and other forms of training. Supervision arrangements should be identified and in force.

FACTORS FOR CONSIDERATION IN A WORK ACTIVITY RISK ASSESSMENT

Work activities take many forms, such as maintenance operations, manual handling, the use of display screen equipment, the operation of fork-lift trucks in loading and unloading, cleaning operations, redecoration of workplaces and constrution-related activities, to name but a few. Certain work activities undertaken on regular basis, such as window cleaning or vehicle loading operations, can be subject to a generic risk assessment, whereas other activities of a specialised nature may require a more specific activity risk assessment.

The more common forms of work activity and factors for consideration are dealt with below.

Maintenance

There should be isolation procedures for plant, machinery and energy sources, a safe system of work, including the use of permits to work and method statements for work in isolated locations involving safe access, safe working positions, and competent persons appointed, where appropriate.

Welding

Portable extraction and filtration units should be used, environmental monitoring of welding area(s) should be undertaken, the provision and use of appropriate PPE, such as hearing protection, visors, gloves, one-piece overalls and respiratory protection, should be assured, flammable gases and materials should be properly used, barriers / screens installed and such work should be carried out in isolated areas and confined spaces. The oxygen enrichment risks should be properly dealt with and the integrity of the welding equipment itself, the size and integrity of the main and secondary cables, the terminals and connectors, the protection of terminal and live components and the capacity of the earthing circuits should all be maintained.

Catering

Floors should be clean with a non-slip finish and drainage. Housekeeping levels should be high. There should be guards on equipment such as meat slicers. The use of knives, cleavers, etc., storage of equipment, lighting arrangements and fire hazards should all be according to the regulations.

Mobile handling operations

There should be trained and authorised drivers, the level of supervision and control should be adequate and safe working procedures should be in place. PPE, such as safety footwear, should be provided and used. There should be procedures in place for when trucks are unattended, compliance with maximum rated load capacity, security of keys, no improper use of trucks as working platforms and adequate maintenance arrangements, testing and examination. The conditions of floors and roadways, design of ramps and gradients, width of aisles, lighting arrangements, parking arrangements, layout and design of operating areas, segregation of pedestrians from fork-lift truck routes, warning signs, windows or ports in rubber doors, use of barriers around vulnerable structures and equipment and battery charging arrangements should all be according to the regulations.

Work at heights

Ladders, safety harnesses, suspended cradles, scaffold materials, crawl boards and safety nets should be in good condition and used safely, there should be adequate inspection and maintenance of scaffolds, eyebolts should be provided at windows and, in addition, ladders should be set at the correct pitch and fixed securely. Work on or adjacent to fragile roofs should be safely carried out, there should be edge protection to flat roofs and openings in same, appropriate action should be taken in adverse weather conditions and PPE, such as safety boots and helmets fitted with chin straps, should be provided and used.

THE OUTCOME OF WORKPLACE AND WORK ACTIVITY RISK ASSESSMENTS

The outcome of these types of risk assessment must be the identification of the key or principal risks, which must be specified in the risk assessment document (see the examples of workplace risk assessment and work activity risk assessment forms in Figures 6.1 and 6.2 (overleaf) respectively).

Both forms of risk assessment will further identify information and authorisation requirements in respect of emergency procedures, training standards, safe systems of work, safety notices and current reference documents, such as ACOPs and HSE Guidance Notes. In certain cases, some form of record keeping requirement may be indicated.

The *risk assessment summary* (see Figure 6.3 (overleaf) for an example), which can apply to both workplace and work activity risk assessments, should identify the principal risks, such as fire, and any specific risks, for example, contact with fork-lift trucks. It must further state, quite specifically, the remedial action necessary on immediate, short-term (say, 28 days), medium-term (such as 6 months) and long-term (over 12 months) bases.

WORKPLACE RISK ASSESSMENT

No. ________ *Date* ________________ *Valid until* ____________________

1 Department/work area
2 Work activities in the workplace
3 Key risks
4 Risk assessment (based on identified hazards):

	Risk rating
• fire protection	
• emergency procedure	
• vehicle movements	
• electrical installations	
• pressure systems	
• welfare amenity provisions	
• environmental factors	
• articles and substances	
• falls and falling objects.	

5 Information and authorisation:
- emergency procedures
- training standards
- safe systems of work
- safety notices
- reference documents.

6 Record keeping requirements

Date *Assessor*

• **FIG 6.1 Example of a workplace risk assessment form**

WORK ACTIVITY RISK ASSESSMENT

No. ________ *Date* ________________ *Valid until* ____________________

1 Department/work area

2 Work activity

Responsible person

3 Key risks

4 Risk assessment (based on identified hazards):

	Risk rating
• work equipment	
• machinery	
• display screen equipment	
• manual handling	
• hazardous substances	
• noise and vibration	
• human factors	
• environmental factors	
• mobile handling equipment	
• electrical installations.	

5 Information and authorisation:

- emergency procedures
- training standards
- safe systems of work
- safety notices
- reference documents.

6 Record keeping requirements

Date *Assessor*

• **FIG 6.2 Example of a work activity risk assessment form**

RISK ASSESSMENT SUMMARY

Risk assessment no.

Work activity/workplace ______________________________

Date of assessment ______________ *Assessor* ______________

Principal risks

Specific risks

Remedial action

1 Immediate

2 In the short term (28 days)

3 In the medium term (6 months)

4 In the long term (over 12 months)

Information, instruction and training requirements

Supervision requirements

Date of next review ______________________

● **FIG 6.3 Example of a risk assessment summary form**

Inevitably, a risk assessment will indicate information, instruction and training requirements for employees and others, together with any general or specific supervision requirements. These requirements should be specified.

Finally, the date of the next review of the risk assessment should be indicated in the summary.

Risk assessment action plan

At the completion stage of the risk assessment exercise, it is advisable to prepare a risk assessment action plan (see Figure 6.4 for an example). This plan should identify each workplace and work activity assessed, the action required, target dates, the person responsible for ensuring that the action is taken and the date of completion of the required action.

RISK ASSESSMENT ACTION PLAN				
Workplace/activity hazard	*Action required*	*Target date*	*Action by*	*Completed by*

Date *Next review before*

• FIG 6.4 Example of a risk assessment action plan

7

Work equipment risk assessments

Work equipment is defined in the *Provision and Use of Work Equipment Regulations 1992 (PUWER)* as meaning any machinery, appliance, apparatus or tool and any assembly of components that, in order to achieve a common end, are arranged and controlled so that they function as a whole. On this basis, work equipment can include items such as vehicles, power presses, laboratory apparatus, an automatic car wash and simple hand tools, such as a screwdriver.

While there is no specific duty to assess the risks from work equipment under PUWER, the duty is implied under regulation 5 (suitability of work equipment) and consideration must be given to the general duty to assess risk under the MHSWR (see further Chapter 1, The generic and specific duties to assess risks). Furthermore, evidence of the need for specific work equipment risk assessments may be identified as a result of the more general risk assessment undertaken under the MHSWR.

WHICH EQUIPMENT SHOULD BE ASSESSED?

It is not suggested that every item of work equipment should be subject to an assessment. However, there may be certain items of equipment where such an assessment may be appropriate, particularly at the selection stage. The reasons for the assessment could include the relative newness of design or function of the equipment, a complicated maintenance procedure for it, the need to ascertain training and information requirements for its use and whether its use should be restricted to designated trained users.

FACTORS FOR CONSIDERATION IN A WORK EQUIPMENT RISK ASSESSMENT

This form of assessment should follow the requirements of the PUWER, not only with regard to the relative suitability of work equipment but also in line with the duties relating to specific risks, dangerous parts of machinery, specified hazards, the various forms of control incorporated in the equipment and the requirement to provide information and instruction. The various factors are summarised below and in Figure 7.1.

Suitability

The equipment should be constructed or adapted so as to be suitable for the purpose for which it is used or is to be used, be selected on the basis of current working conditions, health risks and any additional risks posed by its use and used only for operations and under conditions for which it is suitable.

Maintenance

There should be a system for maintaining equipment in an efficient state, efficient working order and in good repair and maintenance logs should be kept to record maintenance details.

Specific risks

Equipment with restrictions on its use should only be used by designated and trained users. Equally, repairs, modifications or servicing should be undertaken by designated persons.

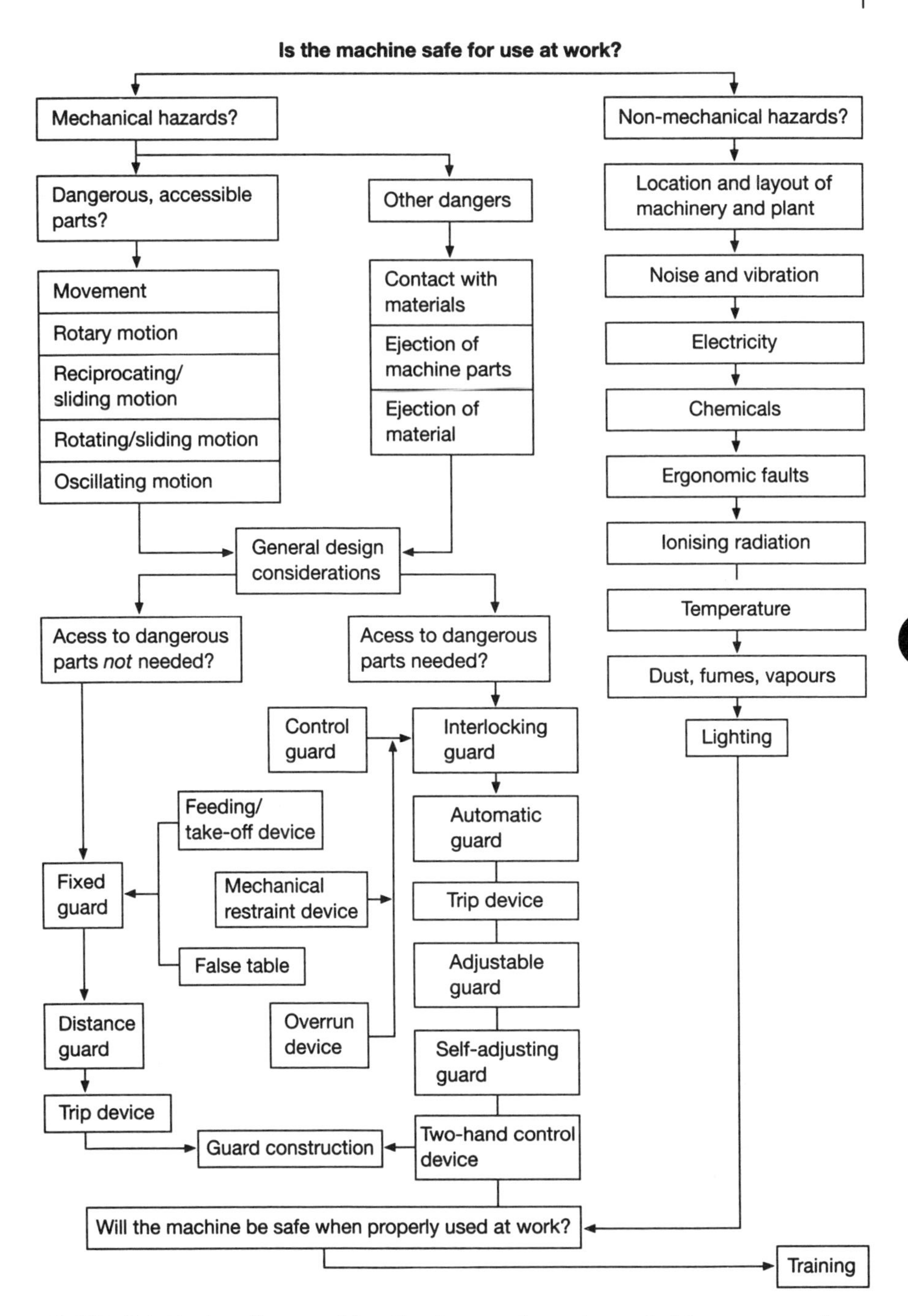

FIG 7.1 Factors for consideration in a work equipment risk assessment

7

Information and instructions

Information and instructions should be available to users, managers and supervisors and should be readily comprehensible to users. They should instruct on the conditions in which and methods by which equipment may be used, indicate foreseeable abnormal situations, and provide conclusions from experience in using the same equipment.

Training

All users, managers and supervisors should be adequately trained in the correct methods of use of equipment, any risks arising from its use and any necessary precautions.

Dangerous parts of machinery

Effective measures should be in place to prevent access to or stop movement of any dangerous part. The hierarchy of guarding in regulation 12 should be followed so that guards and protection devices are suitable, of good construction, sound material and adequate strength, that these are maintained, do not create increased risks, are not easily bypassed or disabled, are situated at sufficient distance from any danger zone, do not restrict viewing of the operating cycle and are constructed or adapted so as to prevent danger.

Specified hazards

Measures should be taken (other than provision of PPE and information, instruction and training) to prevent articles or substances falling or being ejected, the rupture or disintegration of parts, equipment overheating or catching fire and there being unintended or premature discharges or explosions.

High or very low temperatures

Appropriate protection should be provided to prevent burns, scalds or searing.

Controls for starting or making a significant change in operating conditions

Controls should be in place for starting and restarting, changing speed, pressure or other operating conditions that result in increased risks. Deliberate action is required for these controls.

Stop controls

One or more readily accessible stop controls should be provided. Stop controls should operate immediately, sources of energy should be isolated where necessary and stop controls should have priority over starting and operating controls.

Emergency stop controls

One or more readily accessible stop controls should be fitted and an emergency stop control should have priority over a stop control.

Controls

These should be clearly visible and identifiable, with appropriate markings and be safely located.

Control systems

Systems should be safe in that their operation does not create an increased risk, that any fault or damage or loss of supply of energy source cannot result in an increased risk and they do not impede operation of the stop or emergency stop controls.

Isolation from sources of energy

There should be clearly identifiable and readily accessible means of isolating equipment from sources of energy and reconnection to the energy source should not create a risk.

Stability

Where necessary, equipment should be stabilised by clamping.

Lighting

Suitable and sufficient lighting should be provided where equipment is used.

Maintenance operations

Equipment should be so constructed or adapted as to permit maintenance operations to be carried out when it is shut down or otherwise to be carried out safely.

Markings

Equipment should be marked in a clearly visible manner with health and safety markings.

Warnings

Health and safety warnings and warning devices should be incorporated in equipment and such warning devices should be unambiguous, easily seen and easily understood.

THE RISK ASSESSMENT DOCUMENT

An example of a work equipment risk assessment document is shown in Figure 7.2. This example follows the same format as that provided by the HSE in connection with the Manual Handling Operations Regulations 1992. The risk assessment summary (on page 154) should be completed at the end of the assessment.

WORK EQUIPMENT RISK ASSESSMENT

Item of work equipment ____________________

Plant register no. ____________

Operations for which the work equipment is used ____________

Frequency of use (regular use/irregular use) ____________

Date of assessment ____________ *Assessor* ____________

	Yes/no	*Level of risk*		
		Low	*Medium*	*High*
Suitability (reg. 5) It is constructed or adapted as to be suitable for the purpose for which it is used. It was selected taking into account working conditions, health risks and any additional risks posed by its use. It is used only for operations for which, and under conditions for which, it is suitable. **Maintenance (reg. 6)** It is maintained in an efficient state, in efficient working order and in good repair. The maintenance log, where used, is kept up to date. **Specific risks (reg. 7)** Where it is likely to involve a specific risk: ● its use is restricted to designated trained users ● any repairs, modifications or servicing are undertaken by specifically designated people. **Information and instructions (reg. 8)** Adequate health and safety information and, where appropriate, written instructions, are available to users, managers and supervisors.				

● **FIG 7.2 Example of a work equipment assessment form**

7

	Yes/no	*Level of risk*		
		Low	*Medium*	*High*
The information and, where appropriate, the written instructions for use, include: • the conditions in which, and the methods by which, it may be used • foreseeable abnormal situations and the action to be taken if such a situation were to occur • any conclusions to be drawn from experience in using it. Information and instructions are readily comprehensible to users of the equipment. **Training (reg. 9)** All people who use the equipment, managers and supervisors have received adequate training in the methods that may be adopted when using it, any risks its use may entail and precautions to be taken. **Dangerous parts of machinery (reg. 11)** In the case of machinery, effective measures are taken: • to prevent access to any part of machinery or to any rotating stock-bar • to stop the movement of any dangerous part of machinery or rotating stock-bar before anyone enters a danger zone. The above measures consist of: • the provision of fixed guards • the provision of other guards or protection devices • the provision of jigs, holders,push sticks or similar protection appliances used in conjunction with the machinery • the provision of information, instruction, training and supervision.				

FIG 7.2 (Continued)

	Yes/no	Level of risk		
		Low	Medium	High
All guards and protection devices: • are suitable for their purpose • are of good construction, sound material and adequate strength • are maintained in an efficient state, in efficient working order and in good repair • do not give rise to any increased risk to health or safety • are not easily bypassed or disabled • are situated at sufficient distance from any danger zone • do not unduly restrict the view of the operating cycle of the machinery, where such a view is necessary • are so constructed or adapted that they allow operations necessary to fit or replace parts and for maintenance work, restricting access so that work is allowed only to the area where it is to be carried out and, if possible, without having to dismantle the guard or protection device. **Specified hazards (reg. 12)** Measures listed below are taken to ensure that the exposure of the user to any of the undermentioned risks to his health or safety are either prevented or adequately controlled, namely: • measures other than the provision of personal protective equipment or of information, instruction, training and supervision • include, where appropriate, measures to minimise the effects of the hazard as well as the likelihood of the hazard occurring, with particular reference to: – any article or substance falling or being ejected from the work equipment				

● **FIG 7.2 (Continued)**

	Yes/no	Level of risk		
		Low	Medium	High
– rupture or disintegration of parts of the work equipment – the work equipment catching fire or overheating – the unintended or premature discharge of any article or of any gas, dust, liquid, vapour or other substance that, in each case, is produced, used or stored in the work equipment – the unintended or premature explosion of the work equipment or any article or substance produced, used or stored in it. **High or very low temperature (reg. 13)** The work equipment, its parts and any article or substance produced, used or stored in it that, in each case, is at a high or very low temperature has protection where appropriate so as to prevent injury to any person by burning, scalding or searing them. **Controls for starting or making a significant change in operating conditions (reg. 14)** Where appropriate, equipment is provided with one or more controls for the purposes of: ● starting it, including restarting after a stoppage ● controlling any change in the speed, pressure or other operating conditions where such conditions after the change result in risk to health or safety that is greater than or of a different nature to such risks before the change. Where the above control is required, it is not possible to perform any operation above except by a deliberate action on such control.				

● **FIG 7.2 (Continued)**

	Yes/no	Level of risk		
		Low	Medium	High
Stop controls (reg. 15)				
Where appropriate, equipment is provided with one or more readily accessible controls, the operation of which will bring it to a safe condition in a safe manner.				
Any above control brings it to a complete stop where this is necessary for reasons of health or safety.				
If necessary for reasons of health or safety, any above control switches off all sources of energy after stopping the functioning of the equipment.				
The above control has priority over any control that starts or changes the operating conditions of the equipment.				
Emergency stop controls (reg. 16)				
Where appropriate, it is provided with one or more readily accessible emergency stop controls unless it is not necessary due to the nature of the hazards and the time taken for the work equipment to come to a complete stop as a result of the action of any stop control.				
The control operates in priority to a stop control.				
Controls (reg. 17)				
The controls are clearly visible and identifiable, including by appropriate marking where necessary.				
No control is in a position where any person operating the control is exposed to a risk.				
Where appropriate:				
• the operator of any control is able to ensure from the position of that control that no person is in a place where he could be exposed to a risk as a result of the operation of that control				

● **FIG 7.2 (Continued)**

	Yes/no	Level of risk		
		Low	Medium	High
• systems of work are effective to ensure that, when the equipment is about to start, no person is in a place where he would be exposed to risk • an audible, visible or other suitable warning is given whenever the equipment is about to start. Appropriate measures are taken to ensure that any person who is in a place where he would be exposed to risk as a result of the starting or stopping of work equipment has sufficient time and suitable means to avoid that risk. **Control systems (reg. 18)** All control systems are safe in that: • their operation does not create any increased risk • they ensure that any fault in or damage to any part of the control system or the loss of supply to any source of energy cannot result in additional or increased risk • they do not impede the operation stop control or emergency stop control. **Isolation from sources of energy (reg. 19)** Where appropriate, the equipment is provided with suitable clearly identifiable and readily accessible means to isolate it from all sources of energy. Appropriate measures are taken to ensure that reconnection of any energy source does not expose the user to risk. **Stability (reg. 20)** Where necessary, the equipment, or any part of it, is stabilised by clamping.				

FIG 7.2 (Continued)

	Yes/no	Level of risk		
		Low	Medium	High
Lighting (reg. 21) Suitable and sufficient lighting, which takes account of the operations to be carried out, is provided at the places where the equipment is used. **Maintenance operations (reg. 22)** Appropriate measures are taken to ensure that the equipment is constructed or adapted in such a way that maintenance operations which involve a risk can be carried out while the equipment is shut down or, in other cases: • maintenance operations can be carried out without exposing the maintenance operator to risk • appropriate measures can be taken for the protection of any maintenance operator exposed to a risk. **Markings (reg. 23)** The equipment is marked in a clearly visible manner with any marking appropriate for reasons of health and safety. **Warnings (reg. 24)** The equipment incorporates any warnings or warning devices appropriate for reasons of health and safety. Warnings given by warning devices are unambiguous,easily perceived and easily understood.				

FIG 7.2 (Continued)

RISK ASSESSMENT SUMMARY
Principal risks
Specific risks
Remedial action Immediate In the short term (28 days) In the medium term (6 months) In the long term (over 12 months)
Maintenance requirements
Information, instruction, training and supervision requirements
Date of next review

8

Personal protective equipment risk assessments

Regulation 6 of the *Personal Protective Equipment at Work Regulations 1992 (PPEWR)* require an employer – before choosing any personal protective equipment (PPE) that, by virtue of regulation 4, he is required to ensure is provided – to ensure that an assessment is made to determine whether or not the PPE he intends to provide will be suitable. Reference must be made to the HSE Guidance Notes incorporated with the regulations in determining suitability (see further chapter 1, The general and specific duties to assess risks).

Personal protective equipment (PPE) is defined as meaning all equipment (including clothing affording protection against the weather) that is intended to be worn or held by a person at work and protects him against one or more risks to his health or safety and any addition or accessory designed to meet that objective.

PPE includes both the following, when they are worn for protection of health and safety:

- *protective clothing*, such as aprons, protective clothing for adverse weather conditions, gloves, safety footwear, safety helmets, high-visibility waistcoats, etc
- *protective equipment*, such as eye protectors, life jackets, respirators, underwater breathing apparatus and safety harnesses.

APPLICATION OF THE PPEWR

Table 1 of the HSE Guidance Notes outlines the provisions on the use of PPE.

Conditions	*Application of PPEWR*	*Examples*
Where there are existing comprehensive regulations that require PPE	The PPEWR do not apply.	For example, the COSHH regulations require respirators to be used in certain circumstances.
Where there are no current regulations dealing with PPE.	The PPEWR do apply.	For example, the PPEWR require that chainsaw operators are provided with and wear the appropriate PPE.
Where there are existing but not comprehensive regulations requiring PPE.	The PPEWR apply and complement the existing regulations.	For example, regulation 19 of the Docks Regulations requires the provision of high-visibility clothing when an employee is working in specific areas of a dock. The PPEWR complement this duty by laying down duties about the accommodation of the PPE, training of employees in its use, etc., and may also require the use of high-visibility clothing in any other parts of the dock where there is a risk from vehicle movement.

CLASSIFICATION OF PPE (HSE GUIDANCE NOTES)

PPE is classified according to the following categories.

Head protection

There are four classes of head protection:

- crash helmets, cycling helmets, riding helmets and climbing helmets intended to protect the user in falls
- industrial safety helmets that can protect against falling objects or impact with fixed objects
- industrial scalp protectors (bump caps) that can protect against striking fixed obstacles, scalping or entanglement
- caps, hairnets, etc. that can protect against scalping / entanglement.

Eye protection

There are four classes of eye protection.

- *Safety spectacles* are similar in appearance to prescription spectacles but may incorporate optional sideshields to give lateral protection to the eyes. To protect against impact, the lenses are made from tough, optical-quality plastic, such as polycarbonate. Safety spectacles are generally light in weight and are available in several styles with either plastic or metal frames. Most manufacturers offer a range of prescription safety spectacles, which are individually matched to the wearer.
- *Eyeshields* are like safety spectacles but are heavier and designed with a frameless, one-piece, moulded lens. Vision correction is not possible as the lenses cannot be interchanged. Some eyeshields may be worn over prescription spectacles.
- *Safety goggles* are heavier and less convenient to use than spectacles or eyeshields. They are made with a flexible plastic frame and one-piece lens and have an elastic headband. They afford the eyes total protection from all angles as the whole periphery of the goggles is in contact with the face. Goggles may have toughened glass lenses

or have wide-vision plastic lenses. The lenses are usually replaceable. Safety goggles are more prone to misting than spectacles. Double-glazed goggles or those treated with an anti-misting coating may be more effective where misting is a problem. Where strenuous work is done in hot conditions, 'direct ventilation' goggles may be more suitable. However these are unsuitable for protection against chemicals, gases and dust. 'Indirect ventilation' goggles are not perforated, but are fitted with baffled ventilators to prevent liquids and dust from entering. Indirect ventilation goggles will not protect against gas or vapour.

- *Faceshields* are heavier and bulkier than other types of eye protector but are comfortable if fitted with an adjustable head harness. Faceshields protect the face but do not fully enclose the eyes and therefore do not protect against dusts, mists or gases. Visors on browguards or helmets are replaceable. They may be worn over standard prescription spectacles and are generally not prone to misting. Faceshields with reflective metal screens permit good visibility while effectively deflecting heat and are useful in blast and open-hearth furnaces and other work involving radiant heat.

Foot protection

There are six classes of safety footwear.

- *Safety boots or shoes* are the most common type of safety footwear. They normally have steel toe-caps. They may also have other safety features including slip-resistant soles, steel midsoles and insulation against extremes of heat and cold.
- *Clogs* may also be used as safety footwear. They are traditionally made from beech wood, which provides good insulation against heat and absorbs shock. Clogs may be fitted with steel toe-caps and thin rubber soles for quieter tread and protection against slipping or chemicals.
- *Foundry boots* have steel toe-caps, are heat resistant and designed to keep out molten metal. They are without external features (such as laces) to avoid trapping molten metal blobs and should have Velcro fasteners or elasticated sides for quick release.

- *Wellington boots* protect against water and wet conditions and can be useful in jobs where the footwear needs to be washed and disinfected for hygienic reasons, such as in the food industry. They are usually made from rubber and PVC, which are both warmer and have greater chemical resistance. Wellington boots can be obtained with corrosion-resistant steel toe-caps, rot-proof insoles, steel midsoles, ankle bone padding and cotton linings. They range from ankle boots to chest-high waders.
- *Anti-static footwear* prevents the build-up of static electricity on the wearer. It reduces the danger of igniting a flammable atmosphere and gives some protection against electric shock.
- *Conductive footwear* also prevents the build-up of static electricity. It is particularly suitable for handling sensitive components or substances (such as explosive detonators). It gives no protection against electric shock, however.

Hand and arm protection

Hand and arm protection can be classified according to the basis of its capability to give protection from hazards and fit the wearer.

- *Penetration and abrasion* Gloves made from chain-mail or leather protect against penetration and abrasion. Gloves made from knitted Kevlar will provide protection against cuts, and gloves manufactured from Kevlar needlefelt give good puncture resistance.
- *Thermal protection* Depending on their weight and construction, terrycloth gloves will provide protection against heat and cold. Gloves made from neoprene are good for handling oils in low temperatures. Gloves manufactured from other materials, such as Kevlar, glass fibre and leather, can be used to provide protection at higher temperatures.
- *Fire protection* Chromed leather gloves are fire retardant.
- *Chemical protection* Gloves to protect the wearer from chemicals are available in a range of materials, including rubber, neoprene, nitrile, butyl, PVA, PVC and viton. The degree of protection they provide the wearer against chemical permeation depends on the material

used, its thickness and method of construction. As a general rule, gloves for handling toxic liquids should be chosen on the basis of breakthrough time. This means that the duration of use should not exceed the breakthrough time quoted by the manufacturer of the gloves for the chemical substance concerned. Laboratory testing may be required in order to establish adequacy in some applications. When handling dry powders, any chemically resistant glove may be used. The durability of the gloves in the workplace should also be considered. Some glove materials may be adversely affected by abrasion, for instance.

- *General use gloves* Rubber, plastic or knit fabric gloves are flexible, resist cuts and abrasions, repel liquids and offer a good grip. Rubber gloves allow a sensitive touch and give a firm grip in water or wet conditions. Leather, cotton knit or other general purpose gloves are suitable for most other jobs. General use gloves should only be used to protect against minimal risks to health and safety (such as for gardening and washing-up and similar low-risk tasks).

Protective clothing for the body

Types of clothing used to protect the body include:

- coveralls, overalls and aprons to protect against chemicals and other hazardous substances
- outfits to protect against cold, heat and bad weather
- clothing to protect against machinery, such as chainsaws.

RESPIRATORY PROTECTION AND HEARING PROTECTION

Requirements relating to respiratory protection are covered by the COSHH regulations 1994 and are featured in a health risk assessment required under those regulations. Similar provisions apply in the case of hearing protection, which should be recognised in a noise risk assessment under the Noise at Work Regulations 1989. As such, they do not come within the scope of a PPE risk assessment under the PPEWR.

DISAPPLICATION OF THE REGULATIONS

The regulations do *not* apply in respect of PPE that is:

- ordinary working clothes and uniforms that do not specifically protect the health and safety of the wearer
- an offensive weapon within the meaning of section 1(4) of the Prevention of Crime Act 1953 used as self-defence or as deterrent equipment
- portable devices for detecting and signalling risks and nuisances
- PPE used for protection while travelling on a road within the meaning (in England and Wales) of section 192(1) of the Road Traffic Act 1988, and (in Scotland) of section 151 of the Roads (Scotland) Act 1984
- equipment used during the playing of competitive sports.

Apart from regulation 5, which covers the compatibility of different items of PPE worn at the same time, the regulations do not apply where any of the following regulations apply and in respect of any risk to a person's health or safety for which any of them require the provision or use of PPE, namely the:

- Control of Lead at Work Regulations 1980
- Ionising Radiations Regulations 1985
- Control of Asbestos at Work Regulations 1987
- Control of Substances Hazardous to Health Regulations 1994
- Noise at Work Regulations 1989
- Construction (Head Protection) Regulations 1989.

FACTORS FOR CONSIDERATION IN A PPE RISK ASSESSMENT

This form of assessment follows the requirements of the PPEWR with particular reference to provision and suitability. The various factors for consideration in a PPE risk assessment are outlined below.

Provision and suitability

'Provided' because risks have not been controlled by other means; 'suitable' in that it is appropriate to the risks, takes account of ergonomic requirements and the state of health of the wearer, is capable of fitting the wearer correctly and is effective in preventing or controlling the risk without increasing overall risk.

Compatibility

Equipment is compatible when it is used with other items of PPE and continues to be effective against risks.

Accommodation for PPE

Appropriate accommodation should be provided.

Information, instruction and training

Adequate and appropriate information, instruction and training should be provided for employees to enable them to know the risks the PPE will avoid or limit, the purpose and manner of its use and any action that needs to be taken to ensure that the PPE remains in an efficient state, efficient working order and good repair.

Use of PPE

Safe use procedures should be established. PPE should be used in accordance with training and instructions and returned to its accommodation after use.

Reporting loss or defect

Employees should recognise the need to report loss or defect immediately.

THE RISK ASSESSMENT DOCUMENT

Where a number of employees wear the same PPE, PPE risk assessment lends itself to a generic approach. The example of a risk assessment document shown in Figure 8.1 (overleaf) and the risk assessment summary in Figure 8.2 (on page 166) can be used for this purpose. Reference should also be made to the information in Table 8.1 (on page 167) published by the HSE – it shows the relationship between the requirements of the PPEWR and other regulations that require the provision and use of PPE, such as the Control of Lead at Work Regulations 1980.

PERSONAL PROTECTIVE EQUIPMENT RISK ASSESSMENT

Item of personal protective equipment (PPE) ______________________

Risk exposure situation(s) for which the PPE is provided

____

Frequency of use (regular use/irregular use)

____

Date of assessment ______________ *Assessor* ______________

	Yes/no	*Level of risk*		
		Low	*Medium*	*High*
Provision and suitability (reg. 4) The PPE is provided on the basis that the risks have not been controlled by other means that are equally or more effective. It is suitable in that: ● it is appropriate to the risk or risks involved and the conditions at the place where exposure to the risk may occur ● it takes account of ergonomic requirements and the state of health of the persons who may wear it ● it is capable of fitting the wearer correctly, if necessary, after adjustments within the range for which it is designed ● so far as is practicable, it is effective to prevent or adequately control the risks involved without increasing overall risk.				
Compatibility (reg. 5) Where this item of PPE is used with other items of PPE, such equipment is compatible and continues to be effective against the risks in question.				

● **FIG 8.1 Example of a PPE risk assessment form**

	Yes/no	*Level of risk*		
		Low	*Medium*	*High*
Accommodation for PPE (reg. 8)				
Appropriate accommodation is provided for the PPE when not in use.				
Information, instruction and training (reg. 9)				
Employees using this PPE have been provided with such information, instruction and training as is adequate and appropriate to enable the employees to know: • the risk(s) the PPE will avoid or limit • the purpose and the manner in which the PPE is to be used • any action to be taken by the employee to ensure that the PPE remains in an efficient state, in efficient working order and in good repair.				
Use of PPE				
Procedures operate to ensure that the PPE is properly used by employees. Employees use the PPE provided in accordance with the training received by them and the instructions respecting its use.				
Employees take all reasonable steps to ensure that the PPE is returned to the accommodation after use.				
Reporting loss or defect				
Employees understand the need to report forthwith any loss or obvious defect in the PPE to their employer.				

• **FIG 8.1 (Continued)**

RISK ASSESSMENT SUMMARY
Principal risks
Specific risks
Remedial action 1 Immediate 2 In the short term (28 days) 3 In the medium term (6 months) 4 In the long term (over 12 months)
PPE maintenance and cleaning requirements
Information, instruction, training and supervision requirements
Date of next review

● **FIG 8.2 Example of a PPE risk assessment summary form**

Table 8.1 Example of a risk survey table for the use of personal protective equipment (HSE Guidance Notes)

			Risks																				
			The PPE at Work Regulations 1992 apply except where the Construction (Head) Protection Regulations 1989 apply										*The CLW, IRR, CAW, COSHH and NAW Regulaions* will each apply to the appropriate hazard*										
			Mechanical					*Thermal*															
			Falls from a height	*Blows, cuts, impact, crushing*	*Stabs, cuts, grazes*	*Vibration*	*Slipping, falling over*	*Scalds, heat, fire*	*Cold*	*Immersion*	*Non-ionising radiation*	*Electrical*	*Noise*	*Ionising radiation*	*Dust fibre*	*Fumes*	*Vapours*	*Splashes, spurts*	*Gases, vapours*	*Harmful bacteria*	*Harmful viruses*	*Fungi*	*Non-microbio-logical antigens*
Parts of the body	*Head*	*Cranium*																					
		Ears																					
		Eyes																					
		Respiratory tract																					
		Face																					
		Whole head																					
	Upper limbs	*Hands*																					
		Arms (parts)																					
	Lower limbs	*Foot*																					
		Legs (parts)																					
	Various	*Skin*																					
		Trunk/abdomen																					
		Whole body																					

* The Control of Lead at Work Regulations 1980, The Ionising Radiations Regulations 1985, The Control of Asbestos at Work Regulations 1987, The Control of Substances Hazardous to Health Regulations 1988, The Noise at Work Regulations 1989.

Manual handling risk assessments

Manual handling operations are recognised as being one of the principal causes of physical injury at work. Injuries can include straining of muscles and ligaments, hernias, prolapsed (slipped) intervertebral discs and damage to knee, ankle, shoulder and elbow joints. Rheumatism and arthritis are also commonly associated with manual handling operations. Other external injuries include sprains, cuts, bruises, crush injuries and lacerations to hands, fingers, forearms, ankles and feet.

As indicated in Chapter 1, The general and specific duties to assess risks, there is a legal duty on the employer, under the *Manual Handling Operations Regulations 1992 (MHOR)*, so far as is reasonably practicable, to avoid the need for his employees to undertake manual handling operations at work that involve a risk of their being injured. This may be possible through automation or mechanisation of handling operations or by eliminating the need for handling through, perhaps, changing a process.

Where it is not reasonably practicable to avoid the need for manual handling, the employer must make a suitable and sufficient assessment of all such manual handling operations, having regard to the factors specified in column 1 of Schedule 1 to the regulations and consider the questions specified opposite it in column 2 of that Schedule. These factors are the tasks involved, the nature of the loads, the working environment in which the manual handling operation is undertaken, individual capability and other factors that might affect the operation.

A flow chart to assist in interpretation of the regulations is shown in Figure 9.1.

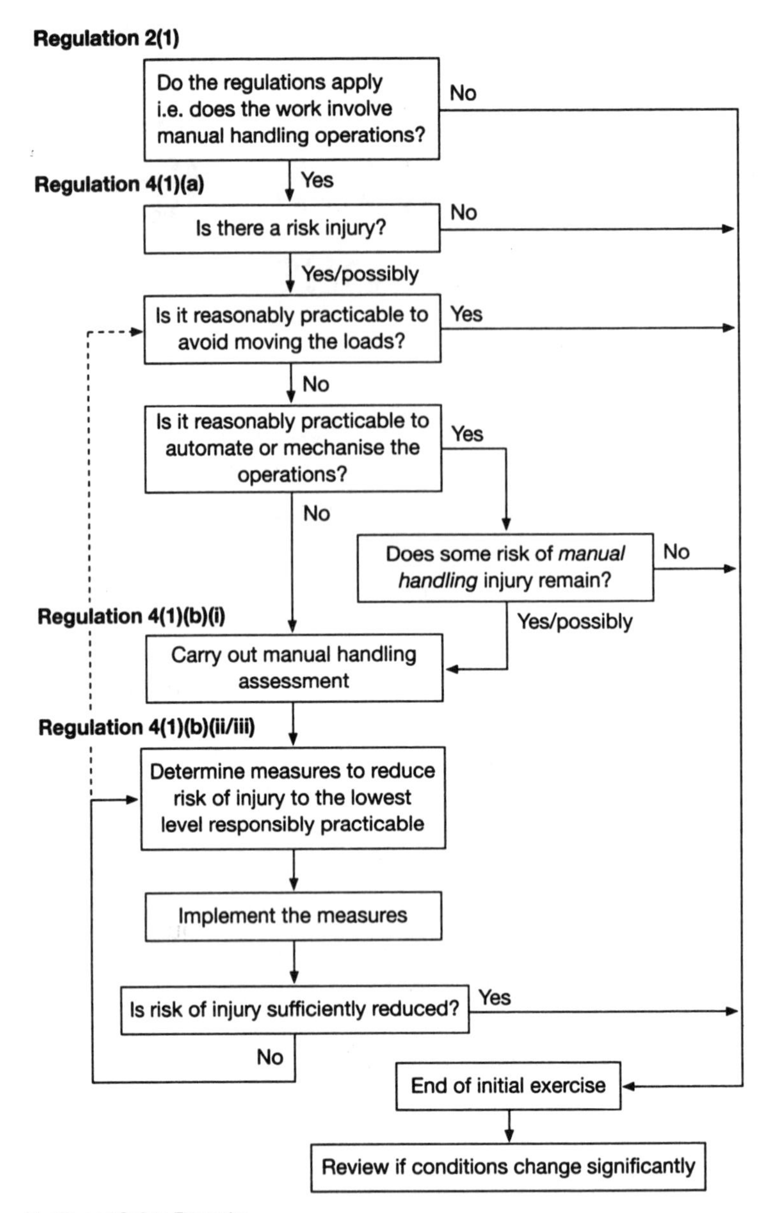

Source: Health and Safety Executive

• FIG 9.1 Flow chart example showing how to follow the MHOR

Appendix 2 of the regulations provides an example of an assessment checklist that is set out in four sections, as follows:

- Section A: preliminary assessment of manual handling operations
- Section B: more detailed assessment, where necessary (which incorporates the factors specified in column 1 of Schedule 1 of the regulations)
- Section C: overall assessment of risk
- Section D: remedial action.

The checklist further incorporates a summary of the assessment.

FACTORS FOR CONSIDERATION IN A MANUAL HANDLING RISK ASSESSMENT

While most manual handling risk assessments will not require completion of the more detailed assessment of section B of the checklist, the various aspects listed in section B are incorporated in the HSE Guidance Notes and detailed below.

The tasks

A consideration of the tasks involved takes account of the potential effects on the body of various movements involved during manual handling operations, namely:

- holding loads away from the trunk
- twisting
- stooping
- reaching upwards
- large vertical movements
- long carrying distances
- strenuous pushing or pulling
- unpredictable movements of loads
- repetitive handling

- insufficient rest or recovery
- a work rate imposed by a process.

The loads

Here it is necessary to consider the nature of the loads. Are they:

- heavy
- bulky, unwieldy
- difficult to grasp
- unstable, unpredictable
- intrinsically harmful (for example, sharp, hot)?

The working environment

Environmental factors can have a significant effect on manual handling in terms of:

- constraints on posture
- poor floors
- variations in levels
- hot, cold, humid conditions
- strong air movements
- poor lighting conditions.

Individual capability

Assessing individual capability is, perhaps, the most difficult and possibly contentious part of the detailed assessment. Does the job:

- require unusual capability
- pose a hazard to those with a health problem
- pose a hazard to those who are pregnant
- call for special information/training?

Other factors

Is movement or posture hindered by clothing or PPE?

RECORDING THE ASSESSMENT

The assessment should be summarised in the block shown in the example assessment checklist drawn up by the HSE shown in Figure 9.2 (overleaf).

Manual handling of loads

ASSESSMENT CHECKLIST

Note: This checklist may be copied freely. It will remind you of the main points to think about while you:

- consider the risk of injury from manual handling operations
- identify steps that can remove or reduce the risk
- decide your priorities for action.

SUMMARY OF ASSESSMENT	*Overall priority for remedial action: (nil/low/medium /high*)*
Operations covered by this assessment	*Remedial action to be taken* ....
....	....
....	....
Locations:	*Date by which action is to be taken* ....
Personnel involved:	*Date for reassessment* ....
Date of assessment:	*Accessor's name* ....*Signature*........................

***circle as appropiate**

Section A: Preliminary:

Q1 Do the operations involve a significant risk of injury? **yes/no***

If 'yes' go to Q2. If **'no'** the assessment need go no further.
If in doubt answer **'yes'**. You may find the guidelines in Appendix 1 helpful.

Q2 Can the operations be avoided/mechanised/automated at reasonable cost? **yes/no***

If **'no'** go to Q3. If **'yes'** proceed and then check that the result is satisfactory.

Q3 Are the operations clearly within the guidelines in Appendix 1? **yes/no***

If **'no'** go to Section B. If **'yes'** you may go straight to Section C if you wish.

(Section B: see next page)

Section C: Overall assessment of risk:

Q1 What is your overall assessment of the risk of injury? **insignificant/low/medium/high***

If not **'insignificant'** go to Section D. If **'insignificant'** the assessment need go no further.

Section D: Remedial action:

Q1 What remedial steps should be taken, in order of priority?

- ....
- ....
- ....
- ....
- ....

And finally:

- complete the summary box above
- compare it with your other manual handling assessments
- decide your priorities for action
- *take action*..........................*and check that it has the desired effect*

• FIG 9.2 Example of a manual handling risk assessment checklist

Section B: More detailed assessment, where necessary

Questions to consider (If the answer to a question is 'yes' place a tick against it and then consider the level of risk)	Yes	**Level of risk** (Tick as appropriate) Low	Medium	High	**Possible remedial action** (Make rough notes in this column in preparation for completing section D)
The tasks – do they involve:					
• holding loads away from the trunk?					
• twisting?					
• stooping?					
• reaching upwards?					
• large vertical movements?					
• long carrying distances?					
• strenuous pushing or pulling?					
• unpredictable movement of loads?					
• repetitive handling?					
• insufficient rest or recovery?					
• a work rate imposed by a process?					
The loads – are they:					
• heavy?					
• bulky/unwieldy?					
• difficult to grasp?					
• unstable, unpredictable?					
• intrinsically harmful (e.g. sharp, hot?)					
The working environment – are there:					
• constraints on posture?					
• poor floors?					
• variations in levels?					
• hot, cold, humid conditions?					
• strong air movements?					
• poor lighting conditions?					
Individual capability – does the job:					
• require unusual capability?					
• hazard those with a health problem?					
• hazard those who are pregnant?					
• call for special information/training?					
Other factors					
Is movement or posture hindered by clothing or personal protective equipment?					

Deciding the level of risk will inevitably call for judgement. The guidelines in Appendix 1 may provide a useful yardstick.

When you have completed section B, go to section C.

• **FIG 9.2 (Continued)**

Display screen equipment risk analyses

Regulation 2 of the *Health and Safety (Display Screen Equipment) Regulations 1992 (HSDSER)* states that every employer shall perform a suitable and sufficient analysis of those workstations that:

- (regardless of who has provided them) are used for the purposes of his undertaking by *users*
- have been provided by him and are used for the purposes of his undertaking by *operators*

for the purpose of assessing the health and safety risks to which those people are exposed in consequence of that use.

Advice on this process is given in the HSE Guidance Notes to the regulations and in the HSE publication *VDUs – An Easy Guide to the Regulations* (see further Chapter 1, The general and specific duties to assess risks).

DISPLAY SCREEN EQUIPMENT – THE RISKS

The three principal risks to health associated with the use of display screen equipment are:

- work-related upper limb disorders
- visual fatigue
- postural fatigue.

Let us look at these risks in more detail.

Work-related upper limb disorders

Work-related upper limb disorders caused by repetitive strain injuries (RSI) were first defined in the medical literature by Bernardo Ramazzini, the Italian father of occupational medicine, in the early eighteenth century. The International Labour Organisation recognised RSI as an occupational disease in 1960 as a condition caused by forceful, frequent, twisting and repetitive movements.

RSI covers some well-known conditions, such as tennis elbow, flexor tenosynovitis and carpal tunnel syndrome. It is usually caused or aggravated by work and is associated with repetitive and overforceful movement, excessive workloads, inadequate rest periods and sustained or constrained postures, resulting in pain or soreness due to the inflammatory conditions of muscles and the synovial lining of the tendon sheath. Present approaches to treatment are largely effective, provided the condition is treated in its early stages. Tenosynovitis has been a prescribed industrial disease since 1975, and the HSE have proposed changing the name of the condition to 'work related upper limb disorder' on the grounds that the disorder does not always result from repetition or strain and is not always a visible injury.

Many people, including assembly workers, supermarket checkout assistants and keyboard operators, are affected by RSI at some point in their lives.

Clinical signs and symptoms include local aching pain, tenderness, swelling and crepitus (a grating sensation in the joint) aggravated by pressure or movement. Tenosynovitis, affecting the hand or forearm, is the second most common prescribed industrial disease, the most common being dermatitis. True tenosynovitis, where inflammation of the synovial lining of the tendon sheath is evident, is rare and potentially serious. The more common and benign form is peritendinitis crepitans, which is associated with inflammation of the muscle-tendon joint that often extends well into the muscle.

Forms of RSI

- *Epcondylitis* Inflammation of the area where a muscle joins a bone.
- *Peritendinitis* Inflammation of the area where a tendon joins a muscle.
- *Carpal tunnel syndrome* A painful condition in the area where nerves and tendons pass through the carpal bone in the hand.
- *Tenosynovitis* Inflammation of the synovial lining of the tendon sheath.
- *Tendinitis* Inflammation of the tendons, particularly in the fingers.
- *Dupuytrens contracture* A condition affecting the palm of the hand, where it is impossible to straighten the hand and fingers.
- *Writer's cramp* Cramps in the hand, forearm and fingers.

Prevention of RSI

Injury can be prevented by:

- the improved design of working areas, such as the positioning of keyboard and VDU screens, heights of workbenches and chairs
- adjustments of workloads and rest periods
- provision of special tools
- health surveillance aimed at detecting early stages of the disorder
- better training and supervision.

If untreated, RSI can be seriously disabling.

Operational stress

This can take the form of both visual fatigue and postural fatigue.

Visual fatigue

Visual fatigue (eye strain) is associated with glare from the display and the continual need to focus and refocus from screen to copy material and back again. The degree of individual fatigue will vary. Vision screening of staff on a regular basis, and as part of a pre-employment health screen, is recommended.

Postural fatigue

Postural fatigue, an outcome of operational stress, may take many forms. It can include backache, neck and shoulder pains associated with poor chair and workstation design and positioning in relation to controls and displays, insufficient leg room and the need to adjust body position.

Other causes of operational stress

Operational stress can also be created by noise from the unit and ancillary equipment, excessive heat and inadequate ventilation.

The degree of operator stress may vary according to age, sex, physical build, attitude to the task, current level of visual acuity, general health and the extent of time spent on tasks not involving attention to a display screen. Users should be encouraged to organise their workloads to permit frequent screen breaks.

FACTORS FOR CONSIDERATION IN A DISPLAY SCREEN RISK ASSESSMENT/ANALYSIS

A risk assessment under the HSDSER should take into account the Schedule to the regulations. This Schedule sets out the minimum requirements for workstations that are contained in the Annex to Council Directive 90/270/EEC on the minimum safety and health requirements for work with display screen equipment. Such an assessment considers the following factors:

- *equipment* display screen, keyboard, work desk or worksurface, work chair
- *environment* space requirements, lighting, reflections and glare, noise, heat, radiation, humidity
- *interface between computer and user/operator* principles of task design, principles of software ergonomics.

THE RISK ASSESSMENT DOCUMENT

The example of a display screen equipment workstation risk assessment form shown in Figure 10.1 (overleaf) has been designed to take into account the above factors. In many cases, where workstations are similar in terms of design, layout, the equipment provided and the actual environment, a generic or model risk assessment can be undertaken. In other cases, a specific risk assessment relating to a particular workstation may be necessary. On completion of the assessment, the risk assessment summary should be recorded and future remedial action planned.

DISPLAY SCREEN EQUIPMENT WORKSTATION RISK ASSESSMENT

	Yes/no	*Level of risk*		
		Low	*Medium*	*High*
The equipment				
Display screen				
Are the characters on the screen well-defined and clearly-formed, of adequate size and with adequate spacing between the characters and lines?				
Is the image on the screen stable, with no flickering or other forms of instability?				
Are the brightness and the contrast between the characters and the background easily adjustable by the operator or user and also easily adjustable to ambient conditions, such as lighting?				
Does the screen swivel and tilt easily and freely to suit the needs of the operator?				
Is it possible to use a separate base for the screen or an adjustable table?				
Is the screen free of reflective glare and reflection liable to cause discomfort to the operator or user?				
Keyboard				
Is the keyboard tiltable and separate from the screen so as to allow the operator or user to find a comfortable working position avoiding fatigue in the arms or hands?				
Is the space in front of the keyboard sufficient to provide support for the hands and arms of the operator or user?				
Does the keyboard have a matt surface to avoid reflective glare?				
Are the arrangements of the keyboard and the characteristics of the keys such as to facilitate the use of the keyboard?				
Are the symbols on the keys adequately contrasted and legible from the design working position?				

• **FIG 10.1 Example of a display screen equipment workstation risk assessment form**

	Yes/no	Level of risk		
		Low	Medium	High
Work desk or worksurface				
Does the work desk or worksurface have a sufficiently large, low-reflectance surface and allow a flexible arrangement of the screen, keyboard, documents and related equipment?				
Is the document holder stable and adjustable and positioned so as to minimise the need for uncomfortable head and eye movements?				
Is there adequate space for operators or users to find a comfortable position?				
Work chair				
Is the work chair stable and does it allow the operator or user easy freedom of movement and a comfortable position?				
Is the seat adjustable in height?				
Is the seat back adjustable in both height and tilt?				
Is a footrest made available to any operator or user who requests one?				
Environment				
Space requirements				
Is the workstation dimensioned and designed so as to provide sufficient space for the operator or user to change position and vary movements?				
Lighting				
Does any room lighting or task lighting ensure satisfactory lighting conditions and an appropriate contrast between the screen and the background environment, taking into account the type of work and the vision requirements of the operator or user?				
Are possible disturbing glare and reflections on the screen or other equipment prevented by co-ordinating workplace and workstation layout with the positioning and technical characteristics of artificial light sources?				

- **FIG 10.1 (Continued)**

	Yes/no	Level of risk		
		Low	Medium	High
Reflections and glare Is the workstation so designed that sources of light, such as windows and other openings, transparent or translucent walls, and brightly coloured fixtures or walls cause no direct glare and no distracting reflections on the screen? Are the windows fitted with a suitable system of adjustable covering to attenuate the daylight that falls on the workstation?				
Noise Is the noise emitted by equipment belonging to any workstation taken into account when a workstation is being equipped, with a view, in particular, to ensure that attention is not distracted and speech is not disturbed?				
Heat Does the equipment belonging to any workstation produce excess heat that could cause discomfort to operators or users?				
Radiation Is all radiation, with the exception of the visible part of the electromagnetic spectrum, reduced to negligible levels from the point of view of operators' or users' health and safety?				
Humidity Are adequate levels of humidity established and maintained?				

• **FIG 10.1 (Continued)**

	Yes/no	Level of risk		
		Low	Medium	High
Interface between computer and operator/user In the designing, selecting, commissioning and modifying of software, and in designing tasks using display screen equipment, does the employer take into account the following principles: ● software must be suitable for the task ● software must be easy to use and, where appropriate, adaptable to the level of knowledge or experience of the user; no quantitative or qualitative checking facility may be used without the knowledge of the operators or users ● systems must provide feedback to operators or users on the performance of those systems ● systems must display information in a format and at a pace that is adapted to operators or users ● the principles of software ergonomics must be applied, in particular to human data processing?				

Comments of assessor

Date *Signature*

10

● **FIG 10.1 (Continued)**

RISK ASSESSMENT SUMMARY
Principal risks
Specific risks
Remedial action 1 Immediate 2 In the short term (28 days) 3 In the medium term (6 months) 4 In the long term (over 12 months)
Information, instruction, training and supervision requirements
Date of next review

● **FIG 10.2 Example of a display screen equipment workstation risk assessment summary form**

Prevention and control strategies

A basic principle in health and safety is that of preventing exposure to a particular risk. If it is not possible to prevent exposure, then the risk must be controlled by the use of various protective measures. A 'safe place' strategy, such as machinery guarding, or the provision of local exhaust ventilation systems to prevent exposure to airborne contaminants, should always be invoked in preference to a 'safe person' strategy, such as health surveillance or the provision of information, instruction and training.

Thus, in the process of risk assessment, once the risk has been identified and assessed, employers must either prevent the risk arising or, alternatively, control it. Much will depend on the magnitude of the risk in terms of the controls applied. In certain cases, the level of competence of operators may need to be considered prior to their undertaking certain work, such as work on electrical systems.

HIERARCHY OF CONTROL

Prohibition

This is the most extreme form of prevention strategy applicable, where there is imminent or serious risk of injury or ill health, and can form the basis for a prohibition notice served by an enforcement officer under the HSWA. As a strategy, prohibition is the strategy adopted in much of the legislation relating to known carcinogens, as well as other hazards where there is no known form of operator protection available. Prohibition, therefore, implies a total ban on a particular system, substance or the operation of a practice or machinery where the danger level is unacceptable.

Elimination

Reviews of the needs of specific processes often reveal potentially hazardous substances or articles the use of which is no longer necessary. These can be eliminated, thereby negating the need for control.

The ideal situation is that all risks should be eliminated. In many cases, however, it is not possible to completely eliminate a risk. Some form of control must, therefore, be applied. The various forms of control, which must be related to the extent of the risks involved, are summarised below.

Substitution

Here, for instance, a less toxic material would be used in place of a more highly toxic one. Typical examples are the substitution of:

- toluene for benzene
- trichloroethane 1.1.1 for carbon tetrachloride.

Whenever possible, substances with an assigned MEL listed in HSE Guidance Note EH 40 should be substituted by substances not quoted in the lists of MELs. Health risk assessment undertaken to comply with the COSHH regulations will, in many cases, identify safer substances that can be substituted for the more dangerous ones.

Enclosure and containment

By these means, the risk is enclosed or contained in such a way that access to it is denied. Thus, the containment of an offending agent or environmental stressor, such as machinery noise, prevents its liberation into the working environment. For instance, total enclosure or containment of a process may be possible by using bulk tanks and pipework to deliver a liquid directly into a closed production vessel.

Similarly, enclosure guarding is used for large machines where guarding of individual risks may be impracticable. Enclosures may take a number of forms, such as acoustic enclosures for noisy machinery, dust enclosures, laboratory fume cupboards and paint spray booths.

Isolation and separation

The isolation of a process using potentially dangerous substances or sources of radiation may simply mean relocating it to a controlled area, thereby separating the majority of the workforce from the risk. In this case, it is necessary to have a system for limiting access into the controlled area to trained and competent operators only. In certain cases, electrical equipment may be isolated in switch rooms or at such a distance from the floor that operators cannot come into contact with it. Alternatively, for example, a high-risk manufacturing plant may be constructed in a remote geographical area to reduce risk.

Environmental control

The employer has a duty to ensure the provision and maintenance of a working environment that is safe and without risks to health. Risks to health and safety may be associated with extremes of temperature, poor levels of lighting and ventilation, noise and vibration, and the presence of airborne contaminants, such as dust, fumes and gases. Structural aspects must also be considered in terms of safe floors, passages and stairways, access to and egress from the workplace and the storage and disposal of waste items. Consideration must be given to the environmental requirements of the WHSWR and other more specific regulations, such as the COSHH regulations.

Ventilation

Infiltration of air into buildings through openings in the fabric, and even planned natural ventilation through windows and other inlets, give no continuing protection wherever toxic fumes, gases, vapours, etc. are emitted from a process. Local exhaust ventilation (LEV) systems must therefore be operated, namely receptor and captor systems (see Figure 11.1). In certain cases dilution ventilation may be appropriate.

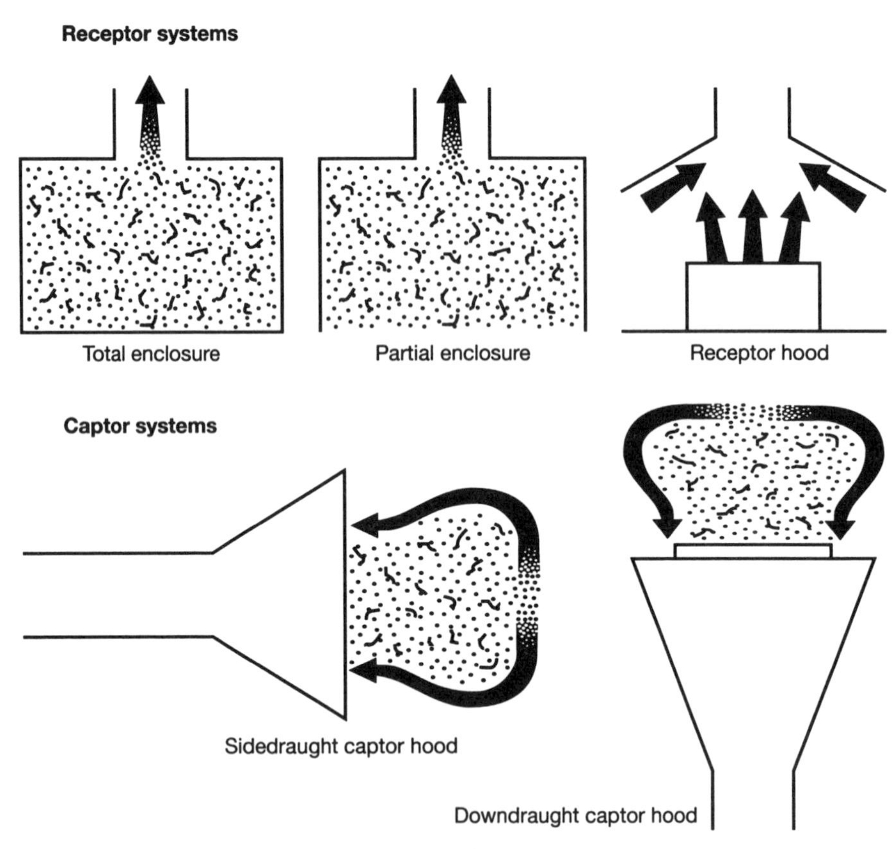

• **FIG 11.1 Local exhaust ventilation (LEV) systems**

Segregation

This is a way of controlling the risks from toxic materials and physical hazards such as noise and radiation. It can take a number of forms.

Segregation by distance (separation)

This is the relatively simple strategy of a person separating himself from the source of the danger. Segregation by distance may be appropriate in the case of noise where, as the distance from the noise source increases, so the risk of occupational deafness reduces. Similar principles apply in the case of radiation. Segregation by distance protects those at secondary risk, if those at primary risk are protected by other forms of control.

Segregation by age

The need for the specific protection of young people has reduced over the last 50 years but, where the risk is marginal, it may be necessary to exclude young people (those under 18 years), particularly females, from certain activities. An example of such segregation occurs in the *Control of Lead at Work Regulations 1980*, which exclude the employment of young persons in prescribed lead processes.

Segregation by time

This is when there is a restriction of certain hazardous operations to periods when the number of workers present is small, for instance at night or during weekends, and when the only workers at risk are those involved in the operation. An example of such an operation is the examination by radiation of very large castings or the stripping of asbestos lagging.

Segregation by sex

There is always the possibility of sex-linked vulnerability to certain toxic materials, particularly in the case of pregnant women where there can be damage to the foetus, such as exists in certain processes involving lead. The *Management of Health and Safety at Work (Amendment) Regulations 1994*, which implement the European Pregnant Workers Directive in the UK, require the risks to pregnant women from work activities to be taken into account in the risk assessment process under the MHSWR.

Machinery safety

The provision and maintenance of appropriate guards and safety devices is essential in preventing injuries associated with operating machinery. The requirements of the PUWER must be complied with, taking into account the HSE Guidance Notes accompanying the regulations, *BS 5304, Safeguarding of machinery*, and other work equipment related to British Standards.

Change of process

Improved design or process engineering can bring about changes to provide better operator protection. This may entail, for instance, liaison with designers, manufacturers and importers of work equipment and of substances used in manufacturing processes. The implementation of techniques such as project safety analysis may also identify the need for changes in a process.

Dilution

There is always some danger in handling chemical compounds in concentrated form. Handling and transport in dilute form reduce the risk. This strategy is appropriate where it is necessary to feed highly concentrated chemicals into processing plant regularly or to carry quantities of dangerous substances for short distances in open containers. Generally, such practices should be discouraged and, wherever possible, eliminated by change of the process. Dilution is a poor form of control strategy.

Neutralisation

This is when a neutralising compound is added to another strong chemical compound, such as an acid or alkali, thereby reducing the immediate danger. This strategy is commonly practised in the transportation of strong liquid waste chemical substances, such as acid-based wastes, where a neutralising compound is added prior to transportation, and in the treatment of industrial process effluent prior to its passing on to a public sewer.

Controlled operation/safe systems of work

This method involves the need for high standards of supervision and control where there may be a high degree of foreseeable risk. Controlled operation may take a number of forms:

- the use of mechanical or remote control handling systems, such as those used with radioactive substances
- the operation of formally established safe systems of work and the use of trained and supervised operators with such systems
- the use of permit-to-work systems, such as for entry into confined spaces
- the restriction of certain activities to highly trained and supervised staff, such as people working in high-voltage switch rooms.

Formally written safe systems of work may be required in certain cases and, where there is a high degree of foreseeable risks, such as entry into confined spaces, a permit-to-work system should be operated.

Cleaning and housekeeping arrangements

The maintenance of high levels of cleaning and housekeeping is an important strategy in the prevention of accidents and occupational disease. Emphasis should be placed, where appropriate, on the use of portable mechanical cleaning equipment rather than on manual methods. Formal cleaning schedules should be operated and housekeeping inspections should feature in the general safety inspection system.

Preventative maintenance

Various hazards may arise during maintenance operations. These can include mechanical hazards (such as traps) arising from machinery, electrical hazards, physical hazards (such as extremes of temperature), chemical hazards, structural hazards (such as openings in floors) and access hazards, possibly arising from work at heights or in confined spaces. Such hazards can be eliminated or controlled principally by means of the operation of safe systems of work, including permit-to-work systems and method statements, the designation of competent persons for certain high-risk activities, controlled areas and various forms of access control.

The absolute duty on employers to operate planned preventative maintenance schemes is implied in the WHSWR and PUWER.

Competent persons

In certain cases, it may be necessary to designate certain people, on the basis of their skills, knowledge and experience, to undertake certain tasks. Such people must be appointed in the case of, for instance, the inspection of scaffolds, excavations, lifting appliances and tackle. The MHSWR require an employer to appoint competent persons to assist him in undertaking the measures he needs to take to comply with the requirements and prohibitions imposed on him by or under the relevant statutory provisions.

Information, instruction and training

There are duties under the HSWA and the majority of regulations to provide information, instruction and training to staff, particularly with regard to the hazards that may exist and the precautions necessary. This should be linked with effective supervision to ensure that the lessons learned are being put into practice.

Warning systems

Warning systems take many forms – from simple safety signs posted at prominent points to more sophisticated devices, such as visible and audible alarms. Safety signs may be classified as prohibition signs, warning signs, mandatory signs and safe condition signs. They should comply with the requirements of the *Safety Signs Regulations 1980* and *BS 5378 Part 1, Safety Signs and Colours – Specifications for Colour and Design*. Fire safety signs should comply with *BS 5499 Part 1, Fire Safety Signs, Notices and Graphic Symbols.*

Personal protective equipment (PPE)

The provision and use of items of PPE, such as eye protection, ear protection, safety boots and shoes, should be seen as the last resort, when

all other measures have failed or, perhaps, as an interim measure until some more permanent form of protection (such as local exhaust ventilation or acoustic enclosure) is provided.

The sole reliance on PPE as a means of protecting people from risks is a highly dangerous strategy. It relies heavily on people who are exposed using or wearing the PPE all of the time they are exposed to the risks, and the majority of people simply do not, or will not, do so. It also calls for a high degree of supervision to ensure that operators use or wear the PPE all the time they are exposed to the risk. PPE should be subject to a risk assessment in compliance with the PPEWR in order to assess the suitability of PPE prior to use.

Health surveillance

Health surveillance concentrates on two main groups of workers:

- those at risk of developing further ill health or disability by virtue of their present state of health, such as people exposed to excessive noise levels
- those actually or potentially at risk by virtue of the type of work they undertake during their employment, for example, radiation workers.

Health surveillance may take many forms:

- pre-employment health screening by an occupational health nurse
- on-going health examinations to assess continuing fitness for work
- medical examinations to detect the presence of occupational diseases or conditions
- where people may be exposed to hazardous substances, various forms of biological monitoring (such as blood and urine tests)
- vision screening of display screen equipment users.

The need for health surveillance may be identified from risk assessments undertaken at an earlier stage under the MHSWR and COSHH regulations.

Personal hygiene

In certain situations, a high level of personal hygiene may be required by operators with a view to preventing, for instance, hand-to-mouth contamination while handling hazardous substances.

Personal hygiene control measures include:

- strict control over decontamination procedures, particularly before eating, drinking, smoking or leaving the premises when work finishes
- a prohibition on eating, drinking and smoking wherever there may be a risk of hand-to-mouth contamination
- use of barrier creams and other forms of skin protection directly related to the risks
- a total prohibition on operators wearing contaminated protective clothing away from the premises and when returning home
- training at induction and on a regular basis thereafter in the principles of personal hygiene and its relationship to existing health risks.

Welfare amenity provisions

The provision and maintenance of well-designed welfare amenities is an important support strategy. Sanitary conveniences, washing facilities, drinking water provision, accommodation for clothing, facilities for changing clothing and for rest and the taking of meals should meet the requirements of the WHSWR and ACOP. In certain high-risk situations, a standard of provision in excess of the minimum legal standard may be required.

Bibliography and further reading

Chapter 1

Health and Safety Executive, *A Guide to the Health and Safety at Work, etc. Act 1974: Guidance on the Act* (HMSO, 1990)

Health and Safety Executive, *Noise Guide No. 3: Equipment and Procedures for Noise Surveys* (HMSO, 1990)

Secretary of State for Employment, *The Control of Substances Hazardous to Health Regulations 1994* (HMSO, 1994)

Secretary of State for Employment, *The Health and Safety at Work, etc. Act 1974* (HMSO, 1974)

Secretary of State for Employment, *The Health and Safety (Display Screen Equipment) Regulations 1992* (HMSO, 1992)

Secretary of State for Employment, *The Management of Health and Safety at Work Regulations 1992* (HMSO, 1992)

Secretary of State for Employment, *The Manual Handling Operations Regulations 1992* (HMSO, 1992)

Secretary of State for Employment, *The Noise at Work Regulations 1989* (HMSO, 1989)

Secretary of State for Employment, *The Personal Protective Equipment at Work Regulations 1992* (HMSO, 1992)

Secretary of State for Employment, *The Provision and Use of Work Equipment Regulations 1992* (HMSO, 1992)

Secretary of State for Employment, *The Workplace (Health, Safety and Welfare) Regulations 1992* (HMSO, 1992)

Stranks, J., *Health and Safety Law* (Pitman Publishing, 1994)

Chapter 2

Deacon, S., *Health Surveillance at Work* (Technical Communications (Publishing) Limited

Health and Safety Commission, *A Guide to Managing Health and Safety in Construction* (HSE Books, 1995)

Health and Safety Commission, *Managing Construction for Health and Safety: Approved Code of Practice* (HMSO, 1995)

Health and Safety Commission, *Management of Health and Safety at Work; Approved Code of Practice: Management of Health and Safety at Work Regulations 1992* (HMSO, 1992)

Health and Safety Executive, *Our Health and Safety Policy Statement; Writing Your Health and Safety Policy Statement; Guide to Preparing a Safety Policy Statement for a Small Business* (HMSO, 1989)

Secretary of State for Employment, *The Management of Health and Safety at Work Regulations 1992* (HMSO, 1992)

Stranks, J., *Handbook of Health and Safety Practice* (Pitman Publishing, 1994)

Stranks, J., *Human Factors and Safety* (Pitman Publishing, 1994)

Stranks, J., *Management Systems for Safety* (Pitman Publishing, 1994)

Chapter 3

Amis, H., and Booth, R. T., *Monitoring Health and Safety Management* (Institution of Occupational Safety and Health, 1991)

Health and Safety Commission, *Management of Health and Safety at Work; Approved Code of Practice: Management of Health and Safety at Work Regulations 1992* (HMSO, 1992)

Health and Safety Executive, *Five Steps to Risk Assessment* (HSE Enquiry Points, 1994)

Health and Safety Executive, *Successful Health and Safety Management* (HMSO, 1991)

Stranks, J., *Handbook of Health and Safety Practice* (Pitman Publishing, 1994)

Stranks, J., *Management Systems for Safety* (Pitman Publishing, 1994)

Chapter 4

Health and Safety Commission, *Approved Code of Practice: Safety Data Sheets for Substances and Preparations Dangerous for Supply: Guidance on Regulation 6 of the Chemicals (Hazard Information and Packaging for Supply) Regulations 1994* (HSE Books, 1995)

Health and Safety Commission, *The Approved Supply List: Information Approved for the Classification and Labelling of Substances Dangerous for Supply* (HSE Books, 1994)

Health and Safety Commission, *General COSHH ACOP (Control of substances hazardous to health), Carcinogens ACOP (control of carcinogenic substances), Biological Agents ACOP (Control of biological agents): Control of Substances Hazardous to Health Regulations 1994* (HSE Books, 1995)

Health and Safety Commission, *Guidance on Regulations: Approved Guide to the Classification and Labelling of Substances and Preparations Dangerous for Supply: Chemicals (Hazard Information and Packaging for Supply) Regulations 1994* (HSE Books, 1994)

Health and Safety Executive, *The Complete Idiot's Guide to CHIP 2: Chemicals (Hazard Information and Packaging for Supply) Regulations 1994* (HSE Books, 1995)

Health and Safety Executive, *Guidance Note EH 40: Occupational Exposure Limits* (HSE Books, 1994)

Health and Safety Executive, *Read the Label: How to Find Out if Chemicals Are Dangerous* (HSE Books, 1995)

Health and Safety Executive, *The Popular Guide: CHIP for Everyone* (HSE Books, 1994)

Health and Safety Executive, *Why Do I Need a Safety Data Sheet?* (HSE Books, 1995)

Secretary of State for Employment, *The Chemicals (Hazard Information and Packaging for Supply) Regulations 1994* (HMSO, 1995)

Secretary of State for Employment, *The Control of Substances Hazardous to Health Regulations 1994* (HMSO, 1994)

Stranks, J., *Occupational Health and Hygiene* (Pitman Publishing, 1995)

Chapter 5

Department of Environment, *Environmental Protection Act 1989* (HMSO, 1989)

Department of Health and Social Security, *Social Security (Industrial Injuries) (Prescribed Diseases) Regulations 1985* (HMSO, 1985)

Health and Safety Executive, *Noise at Work: Noise Guide No. 1: Legal Duties of Employers to Prevent Damage to Hearing; Noise Guide No. 2: Legal Duties of Designers, Manufacturers, Importers and Suppliers to Prevent Damage to Hearing; The Noise at Work Regulations 1989* (HMSO, 1989)

Health and Safety Executive, *Noise at Work: Noise Guide No. 3: Equipment and Procedures for Noise Surveys; Noise Guide No. 4: Engineering Control of Noise; Noise Guide No. 5: Types and Selection of Personal Ear Protectors; Noise Guide No. 6: Training for Competent Persons; Noise Guide No. 7: Procedures for Testing Noisy Machinery; Noise Guide No. 8: Exemptions from Certain Requirements of the Noise at Work Regulations 1989* (HMSO, 1990)

Health and Safety Executive, *100 Practical Applications of Noise Reduction Methods* (HMSO, 1983)

Secretary of State for Employment, *The Noise at Work Regulations 1989* (HMSO, 1989)

Stranks, J., *Handbook of Health and Safety Practice* (Pitman Publishing, 1994)

Stranks, J., *Occupational Health and Hygiene* (Pitman Publishing, 1995)

Chapter 6

Department of Employment, *The Workplace (Health, Safety and Welfare) Regulations 1992* (HMSO, 1992)

Health and Safety Commission, *Workplace Health, Safety and Welfare: Approved Code of Practice: Workplace (Health, Safety and Welfare) Regulations 1992* (HMSO, 1992)

Stranks, J., *Handbook of Health and Safety Practice* (Pitman Publishing, 1994)

Chapter 7

British Standards Institution, *Code of Practice: Safeguarding of machinery: BS 5304* (BSI, 1988)

Department of Employment, *The Provision and Use of Work Equipment Regulations 1992* (HMSO, 1992)

Health and Safety Executive, *Work Equipment: Guidance on Regulations: Provision and Use of Work Equipment Regulations 1992* (HMSO, 1992)

Stranks, J., *Safety Technology* (Pitman Publishing, 1996)

Stranks, J., *Handbook of Health and Safety Practice* (Pitman Publishing, 1994)

Chapter 8

Department of Employment, *The Personal Protective Equipment at Work Regulations 1992* (HMSO, 1992)

Health and Safety Executive, *Guidance Note HS(G)53: Respiratory Protective Equipment: A Practical Guide for Users* (HMSO, 1990)

Health and Safety Executive, *Personal Protective Equipment at Work; Guidance on Regulations: Personal Protective Equipment at Work Regulations 1992* (HMSO, 1992)

Stranks, J., *Handbook of Health and Safety Practice* (Pitman Publishing, 1994)

Chapter 9

Department of Employment, *The Manual Handling Operations Regulations 1992* (HMSO, 1992)

Health and Safety Executive, *Getting to Grips with Manual Handling* (HSE Enquiry Points, 1993)

Health and Safety Commission, *Guidance on Manual Handling of Loads in the Health Services* (HMSO, 1992)

Health and Safety Executive, *Lighten the Load: Guidance for Employees on Musculoskeletal Disorders* (HSE Enquiry Points, 1992)

Health and Safety Executive, *Manual Handling: Guidance on Regulations: Manual Handling Operations Regulations 1992* (HMSO, 1992)

Stranks, J., *Handbook of Health and Safety Practice* (Pitman Publishing, 1994)

Chapter 10

Department of Employment, *The Health and Safety (Display Screen Equipment) Regulations 1992* (HMSO, 1992)

Health and Safety Executive, *Display Screen Equipment Work: Guidance on Regulations: Health and Safety (Display Screen Equipment) Regulations 1992* (HMSO, 1992)

Health and Safety Executive, *Visual Display Units* (HMSO, 1983)

Health and Safety Executive, *Working with VDUs* (HSE Enquiry Points, 1992)

Chapter 11

British Standards Institution, Code of Practice: *Safeguarding of Machinery: BS 5304* (BSI, 1988)

British Standards Institution, *Fire Safety Signs, Notices and Graphic Symbols: BS 5499 Part 1* (BSI, 1980)

British Standards Institution, *Safety Signs and Colours – Specifications for Colour and Design: BS 5378 Part 1* (BSI, 1980)

Department of Employment, *Safety Signs Regulations 1980* (HMSO, 1980)

Stranks, J., *Handbook of Health and Safety Practice* (Pitman Publishing, 1994)

Stranks, J., *Occupational Health and Hygiene* (Pitman Publishing, 1995)

Index

Complete coverage for NEBOSH and beyond

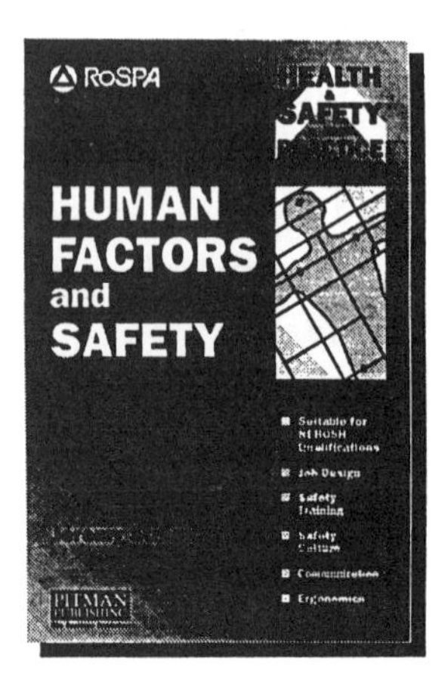

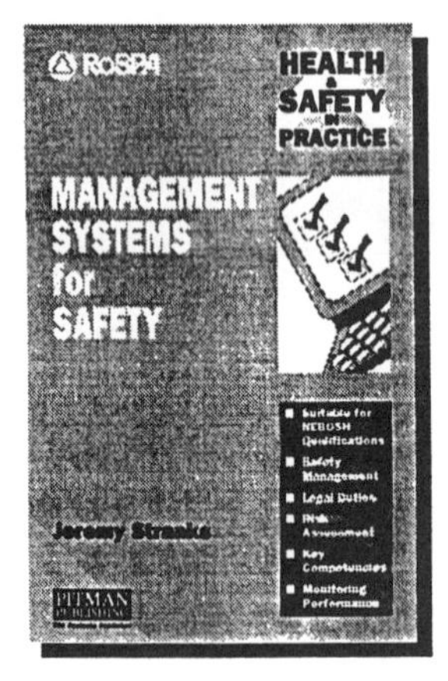